TEARS AND SMILES

MARTYN LEWIS

Tears and Smiles

THE HOSPICE HANDBOOK

Foreword by HRH The Duchess of Kent

MICHAEL O'MARA BOOKS LIMITED

To the memory of Sylvia, whom I
never really knew, and Bruce, whom
I wish I had known better.

First published in Great Britain by
Michael O'Mara Books Limited
9 Lion Yard
11–13 Tremadoc Road
London SW4 7NF

Copyright © 1989 by Martyn Lewis

A CIP catalogue record for this book is available from the
British Library.

ISBN 1-85479-060-9

Editor: Rosemary Pettit
Design: James Campus

Typeset by Florencetype Limited, Kewstoke, Avon
Printed and bound in Great Britain
by Mackays of Chatham PLC

CONTENTS

Foreword by Her Royal Highness the Duchess of Kent   7

Acknowledgements   9

Introduction   11

1. What is a Hospice? – Shattering the Myth   13

2. How It All Began – A Brief History
   of Hospices in Britain   17

3. Inside a Hospice – The Patients' View   25

4. Day Hospices   27

5. Hospice Help in Your Own Home   30

6. Help for Relatives – Bereavement Counselling   33

7. Aids and the Hospice Movement   41

8. Hospice Help for Children   47

9. Politics and Hospices – The Party Policies   58

    The Conservative Party: the Prime Minister   58

    The Labour Party: Mr Neil Kinnock   59

    The Democrats: Mr Paddy Ashdown   62

    The SDP: Dr David Owen   65

10. Setting up a Hospice – the Problems and Pitfalls   67

11. Fund-raising for Your Local Hospice   78

12. How to Obtain Admission to a Hospice   85

13. The Hospice Charities – How They Can Help   87

    BACUP   87

    CancerLink   87

    Cancer Relief Macmillan Fund   88

    Help the Hospices   88

    The Lisa Sainsbury Foundation   89

    The Marie Curie Memorial Foundation   89

    The Sue Ryder Foundation   89

14. Other Useful Charities and Contacts   91

Conclusion   108

Further Reading   110

Hospice Directory   111

    County List   111

    Town and City List   119

Illustration sources   176

Hospices have long been in need of a single
reference book to explain their purpose to those who
might need their help. Cancer or other life-threatening
illnesses can strike at any time. Although assistance
is usually at hand, it can be some time before the
patient and family become aware of its full range.
This much needed layman's guide brings directly into
the home information about every conceivable service
that could help to ease the burden.

Tremendous advances have been made in the
treatment of people with such illnesses. The rates of
cure are so much higher than they used to be - and
developments in pain control spare patients from
suffering unnecessarily. Hospices and home care nurses
have helped to set new standards of care. This book
shows the unique quality of their work, and the warmth,
friendship and skill available from the staff and
volunteers who make up this great and growing
movement.

My hope for the future is that everyone should
fully appreciate what a hospice has to offer - that it
is a haven for young or old in need of short or long
term care. A haven, too, for relatives in the
knowledge that the patient is secure. So often have I
heard patients say "I feel safe; I feel secure; in this
place I have found peace and happiness".

The title of the book, "Tears and Smiles",
encompasses all that I would seek to impart to the
general public. Tears and smiles run so closely
together. Having read this book may your tears also
mingle with smiles from the discovery that there is
loving care to surround you at every turn.

Katharine

Acknowledgements

I am no expert on hospices and have tried to approach the subject with the fresh, enquiring mind of the people for whom this is written; so I am deeply grateful for the help of many people within the hospice movement who have been generous with their time and advice. My warmest thanks go to the staff of numerous hospice units around the country who took time to complete a detailed survey questionnaire and bombarded me with thoughts and suggestions that sprang from years of front-line experience; Dame Cicely Saunders, Professor Eric Wilkes and the Rev. Tom Scott, whose meticulous combing of my early draft manuscript corrected several points of detail and emphasis; all the hospice charity officials, organizers and researchers who inundated me with material which they allowed me to use or adapt and, subsequently, ran an 'examiner's' eye across some or all of the chapters – in particular Susan Butler, Paul Rossi, Major-General Michael Carleton-Smith, Mother Frances Dominica, Dr Derek Doyle, Owen Hagan, Nicholas Grant, Derek Spooner, Caspar Thomson, Christopher Spence, Dr Veronica Moss, Jo Hearn, Jill Pomerance and Dr Bob Woodward; Rosemary Harper and her team at the Department of Community Medicine in the University of Sheffield's Medical School for allowing me to raid their definitive guide on setting up a hospice; Avril Jackson and Ann Eve, founts of all knowledge at the Hospice Information Service at St Christopher's Hospice; Susan Munday for her meticulous work in sifting and sorting the results of the special hospice survey; Frank Hill and Barry Lunt, statistical and research gurus of the movement, whose work provided me with much fodder, although we never actually met; the Prime Minister and Conservative leader Margaret Thatcher, the Labour leader Neil Kinnock, the Democrat leader Paddy Ashdown, and the SDP leader David Owen for providing, exclusively for this book, their most detailed policy statements yet on the hospice movement; Yoshi Shimazu and John Cole for use of their splendid photographs; Cancer Relief Macmillan Fund, Help the Hospices and

CLIC for access to their picture libraries; and the Lisa Sainsbury Foundation and Cancer Relief Macmillan Fund for their meticulous logging of all forms of hospice help. I am also deeply grateful to HRH The Duchess of Kent for agreeing to write the foreword; to my publisher, Michael O'Mara, for donating his profits from this book to the main hospice charities; to British Telecom, the Halifax Building Society, The Bernard Sunley Charitable Foundation and British Gas for sponsoring the distribution costs; and to my wife Liz for her encouragement and understanding while I locked myself away in front of my computer.

Martyn Lewis, May 1989

INTRODUCTION

Although I did not realize it at the time, this book really began twenty years ago when a young couple about to be married suddenly needed hospice help for a very dear relative. Unaware of the modern hospice movement, which was then in its infancy, we were told about a place which was not in itself a hospice but was run on what we now recognize as hospice principles. Surrounded by peace and quiet, amply endowed with warmth, friendship and love, it was run by some of the most caring people you could hope to meet. Their religious beliefs were not ours – they said this did not matter. Unlike hospices, fees were charged – fees which we could not afford. That, they insisted, did not matter either. They subsequently provided devoted one-to-one nursing care around the clock for a life-lengthening two years in an environment that could not have eased better the pain of parting. So this book is another way of thanking them: a small down-payment on the enormous debt owed across the years, by my family and countless others, both to them and to the many hospices and home-care teams who hourly care for thousands in their time of greatest need.

Although the memory of that time lingered, it was another twelve years before the hospice movement touched again the life of this busy reporter. This time it was a telephone call from the Duchess of Norfolk. She and other leading figures in the hospice movement were forming a new charity, 'Help the Hospices'; they needed a video to explain its work and various production companies had quoted her sums, ranging from £30,000 to £80,000, to make it. Did I know any of the companies? Could I advise her on which one to choose? There was something sad about a new charity spending its first few thousands of pounds on this admittedly vital promotional tool. But, by coincidence, it was what we call a 'thin' time for television news – not much seemed to be happening in the world. My then employers, Independent Television News, had frustrated film crews hungry for work. I asked my editor, David Nicholas, if I could borrow a crew 'free' for a week – and a videotape editing suite for another week. He readily agreed – and the video was made.

Shortly after that, at a private ITN dinner for the Duke and Duchess of Kent, the Duchess discovered I had made this video and I, in turn, discovered Her Royal Highness's deep involvement in the hospice movement. Out of that conversation came the unique opportunity to make a television news report of one of the Duchess's regular visits to Helen House, the world's first children's hospice. And if, as we were told, that report had a profound effect on many who saw it, how much greater was the effect on those involved in the filming itself? The hospice movement had me hooked!

My research for those – and other programmes – brought me into contact with the many charities that are the backbone of the movement. All do amazing work; all provide detailed information about that work; but all are, quite properly, busy doing their own thing. So although there were many published documents and brochures in this field, there was no first point-of-call, no simple, all-embracing guide for the ordinary man and woman who suddenly needs hospice help and wants not just up-to-date comprehensive details but every conceivable address and telephone number. This book, born from discussions with leading members of the hospice movement almost five years ago, aims to fill that gap.

1. WHAT IS A HOSPICE?
Shattering the Myth

'Hospices are places where tears and smiles walk side by side – it is quite extraordinary.' *H.R.H. The Duchess of Kent*, 19 June 1985.

There can be few phrases that sum up so perfectly and so elegantly the completeness of caring that is at the core of the hospice philosophy. The movement goes out of its way to concentrate thought and effort on the quality of each individual life, seeking to enrich a very precious time and ensuring that people do not give up but really *live* until the very moment they die. And yet many still think of a hospice as that strange grey building up on the hill or behind the trees where people go towards the end of life – the sort of place you hurry past or talk about in hushed whispers, if at all. To those who still believe that, let me tell you, as politely as I can, that you are living in the past; that your prejudice (for that is what it is) is a product of outdated misinformation and gossip, in which fear of a person's (possible) terminal condition has been translated into an irrational fear of the place where that person might go to spend their last months, weeks or days.

In Britain, few people like to talk about death – let alone face it. And yet it is precisely when death becomes a possibility that help is most needed, both for the patient and for the relatives. Hospices – and the remarkable people who run them – offer that help with a degree of understanding, warmth and compassion that is often not possible in busy hospitals where the pressures and priorities are different – where the main emphasis is on cure.

But although, for many people, a hospice will be their last 'home', there are some who will survive to return to their own home – who will respond to their medical treatment beyond all expectations. I once met a remarkable elderly lady called Ivy who had been admitted to a hospice after doctors gave her five months to live. Five years later she had not only confounded the experts but was the life and soul of that particular hospice! For that reason some hospices prefer to be called 'continuing care units' with all the extra hope that that implies. Others prefer to face the worst head-on – and actively help patients, when they are ready, to come to terms with – and prepare themselves for – what may have been diagnosed as inevitable. Whatever the emphasis for the individual patient, they all offer not only extra care, comfort and attention, but also freedom from pain in all its aspects and techniques. It is this reliance on the effective and careful use of drugs to remove pain and provide relief from other distressing symptoms that is the real hallmark of the modern hospice movement in Britain.

Hospices come in all shapes and sizes – from converted Victorian and Georgian houses to modern, purpose-built facilities. They are found in all kinds of places – some are in hospital grounds with all the ease of communication that can bring, while others prefer to move further away to emphasize the distinctiveness of the service they offer. The wards are seldom large and are often supplemented with pleasant, well-equipped, single-bedded rooms.

There are no special qualifications needed for admission to hospices – they are proud to say they 'accept people of all religions, and those with none at all'. And a decision on whether to take in a patient is based solely on an assessment of that person's need – along with, of course, the availability of beds. Some patients stay for just a few days – others for several months. The *average* stay is three weeks. And the nurse/patient ratio is extremely high – emphasizing the high degree of personal attention.

A growing number of hospices have day centres where patients can be dropped off each morning to be looked after, leaving relatives free to pursue a day's work or a day off before returning to collect their loved one in the evening. Very often the local health authority, the council, a charity or the hospice itself will run a daily shuttle bus service – collecting people from their homes and delivering them back there in the evening.

But the fastest-growing aspect of the hospice movement – and one which is generally recognized as pointing the way to much future development – is the tendency to try, wherever possible, to look after people *in their own homes*. This involves having a team of specialist nurses on call twenty-four hours a day, seven days a week, to make regular visits to patients and to respond to phone calls for extra help. Such 'home care' teams work closely with the local hospice if there is one: a few are based in hospitals but the majority are a growing part of the community nursing team.

Whichever hospice service is considered most appropriate for the patient, time is also found for the relatives too. Bereavement counselling – helping people to come to terms with the death of a loved one – begins before that person has died and continues afterwards for as long as is necessary. Often a strong bond develops between helped and helper; this bond encourages relatives to return again and again, for years afterwards, to the hospice to which they feel they owe so much.

The hospice movement grew out of a desire to offer greater help to those suffering from cancer: that remains its main purpose. Medical diagnoses over the years, however, have defined other conditions that can qualify for hospice help, such as motor-neurone disease (which affects the brilliant Cambridge Professor Stephen Hawking and took the lives of the actor David Niven and the former England football manager Don Revie). Some hospices accept MND patients – others do not – a great deal depends on their ability to offer the extra-specialist nursing required by these conditions and the additional pressures that go with them.

Hospices are taking some time to come to terms with the relatively new disease known as 'AIDS'. The government has made it clear that it expects hospices to be in the forefront of caring for AIDS patients. Some hospices argue, however, that as they were set up specifically to help *cancer* patients – and in some cases derive much of their essential charitable funding from people and organizations who wish *specifically* to help such patients – they should not take people with AIDS, especially if they do not have enough beds for all the cancer patients in need. A few compromise by saying they will only accept AIDS patients who *also* have cancer.

Some of this initial reluctance was a product of the ignorance and fear which attended the public discovery of the disease and the virus that caused it. And there is no doubt that these attitudes were largely responsible for the setting up of special hospices e.g., the London Lighthouse and the Mildmay, to deal solely with AIDS cases. One side-effect of this reluctance is that some hospices argue that, if *they* are expected to take AIDS patients, the specialist AIDS hospices should take cancer patients – something which up to now they have refused to do because of the sheer weight of AIDS sufferers knocking on their doors. It has a frustrating 'Catch-22' feel about it. But attitudes are changing – albeit rather more slowly than some would like.

It is now accepted that for AIDS patients the nursing precautions necessary are no more than are already established as normal, good hospice practice. A survey commissioned especially for *The Hospice Handbook* revealed that over half the country's 133 existing in-patient hospices had already made, or are making, arrangements to take some AIDS patients – although thirty-three said firmly they had *no* such plans and thirty-two are still undecided. The issue will provide lively debate within the hospice movement for some time to come – but it seems certain that the number of potential AIDS beds will grow slowly while, at the same time, the views of those who wish to take cancer sufferers only will be respected.

But it must be stressed that the vast majority of patients to be found in hospices for adults are suffering from cancer. Theirs is a need which, by all predictions, is certain to grow. Britain sees a quarter of a million *new* cases of cancer every year (worldwide the figure is six million). Between a quarter and a fifth of all deaths are from cancer. One person out of every three in Britain will get cancer at some time in their lives. And at any one time, in this country alone, there are more than a million people with cancer. Those sort of statistics encourage the widespread belief that cancer is (a) inevitably fatal, (b) causes unrelieved distress and (c) is full of pain. In Britain at the end of the eighties those views could not be more out-of-date.

The fact is that at least a third of all cancers in men are now curable – with women it is higher, just over 40 per cent; one third are preventable and controllable (WHO-1988); and because the treatment of cancer is improving, more patients are surviving longer and are able to live normal lives. But with that increased hope for some comes increased need for others. The over-sixties, whose numbers are rising rapidly, have an above-average number of cancer cases. And for every person who wins the fight against cancer, two will not do so. Inevitably, that means more people with advanced cancer seeking – and depending on – the professionalism, the warmth and the love on offer from the hospices of Britain.

Your first visit to a hospice will, inevitably, be laced with some apprehension and sadness; but I have no doubt you will come away, as I did, agreeing that they are very, very special places where tears and smiles do, indeed, walk side by side.

2. HOW IT ALL BEGAN
A Brief History of Hospices in Britain

From early in the Christian era, a hospice was a place where pilgrims and other travellers could find food and refuge; the religious orders who managed the hospices also cared for the destitute, the sick and the dying. Most closed after the Reformation and those left became alms houses for the elderly or resting places for travellers but by the nineteenth century the few still open provided an alternative, both to the charitable hospitals (which excluded the so-called 'incurables') and to the workhouse infirmaries which catered for the destitute.

The word 'hospice', to describe a place caring solely for dying patients, was first used in 1842, when Mme Jeanne Garnier founded the Dames du Calvaire at Lyons in France. The name was adopted, quite independently, by the Irish Sisters of Charity when they began carrying out similar work in Ireland in 1879; and the establishment of the hospice in Britain as a centre for care of the terminally ill began in 1885 at the Friedenshe Home of Rest, later St Columba's Hospice. Hard on its heels in 1891 came the Hostel of God in Clapham (now Trinity Hospice), staffed by the Sisters of St Margaret. This was the result of an appeal by the Hoare banking family for funds 'to found a home for persons in an advanced stage of a mortal illness' – thus establishing a heavy reliance on charitable giving which continues in the hospice movement to this day. A year later Dr Barrett and the West London Mission opened St Luke's Home (later Hospital) for the Dying Poor. Cardinal Vaughan's expressed concern for the plight of the sick in the slums of London brought the Sisters of Charity across from Ireland. They set up St Joseph's Hospice in Hackney to serve the community in the East End of London – and the first patient, a forty-seven-year-old local tram driver dying of consumption, was carried in by his friends on 14 January 1905.

Concern for the welfare of patients suffering from cancer prompted the formation of two charities destined to have a major impact on the hospice scene. In 1911 Douglas Macmillan, who had watched with increasing anguish the suffering of his dying father, founded the National Society for Cancer Relief and, as early as the 1920s, recognized the need to provide special homes and home-care nurses. Then, in 1948 Squadron-Leader Bernard Robinson, inspired by Winston Churchill's comment that casualties from cancer were far worse than those suffered in the Second World War, gathered together a few like-minded friends and formed the Marie Curie Memorial Foundation, named after the lady who devoted her life to research into radiation and its use in cancer therapy.

A dramatic indication of the scale of the job to be done came from one of the first committees set up by the Marie Curie. Its terms of reference were brief and to the point – 'to make an investigation of the present position of cancer patients being nursed at home, and to make recommendations concerning the best methods of providing the necessary help'. Representatives of the Queen's Institute of District Nursing joined the committee; the co-operation of all Medical Officers of Health was sought and readily given; and it is a measure of the importance placed on the survey that, out of a total of 193 local health authorities, no fewer than 179 gave complete co-operation and some of the rest were only prevented from doing so by staff shortages. Nursing Superintendents and District Nurses across the country organized the completion of questionnaires covering 7050 patients. The first survey of its kind, it was finished in 1952 and revealed an undreamt-of catalogue of distress. It recommended that Marie Curie provide, as a matter of urgency, 'special residential homes for the care of cancer patients – both the seriously ill and for convalescent cases – with skilled nursing care in a non-stressful and cheerful environment'. By the end of the decade the first such homes were up and running. Now there are eleven, nationwide, with special emphasis on rehabilitation, continuing care, pain relief and symptom control.

In 1953 another charity keen to embrace cancer work – the Sue Ryder Foundation – was set up. But its brief and its intended reach stretched into other needy corners of society. An international foundation, it was (and is) dedicated to the relief of suffering on a much wider scale, caring for patients with many different disabilities.

It was at St Joseph's Hospice in the 1950s that Dr (now Dame) Cicely Saunders, as Medical Officer, began to develop techniques of pain control which she had first observed as a medical student while working as a volunteer nurse in St Luke's Hospital. She firmly established that it was possible to achieve better control of pain by giving analgesic drugs at regular intervals *before* the patient appeared to need them. This had the effect of not only alleviating the pain but also avoiding the anxiety which makes it worse. And, although other forms of cancer treatment have subsequently been developed, it is the regular administration of pain-killing drugs, together with the detailed control of other symptoms, and the personalized care of patients and support for their relatives, which has become the hospice trademark. So when Cicely Saunders set up St Christopher's in Sydenham in 1967, as the first research and teaching hospice, it quickly became the acknowledged international pioneer in the field of hospice practice, earning her the unofficial title of Founder of the Modern Hospice movement. She, herself, has always said that her patients – in their needs and achievements – were the real founders. Under her direction hospice work was extended to home care in 1969 and much further work was done to increase understanding of the biological mechanisms of pain-control drugs – opening up a whole new area of specialist medicine.

In tandem with this new emphasis on pain control came a realization of how important it was to help not just the physical suffering of the patient but also the emotional anguish of relatives. New York's system of family support (mainly by social workers) set up by the American Cancer Care organization in the 1950s was visited by Dr Saunders in 1963. But the main plans for proper bereavement services in British hospices came from ideas shared by Dr Colin Murray Parkes at St Christopher's, the Tavistock Centre for Human Relations and CRUSE, a national organization set up in 1959 to help the widowed and their children. The hospice movement was to develop these ideas in its own way, training volunteers who were especially sensitive to the difficulties of watching a loved one endure an often physically debilitating illness. The first of these set out from St Christopher's in 1971.

These twin batons of pain control and bereavement counselling were quickly picked up by people like Professor Eric Wilkes who opened St Luke's Hospice in Sheffield in 1971, and by the National Society for Cancer Relief which backed a whole chain of hospices and special units, starting with Douglas Macmillan Home in Stoke-on-Trent in 1972. Cancer Relief was, by now, moving on other fronts. It made an arrangement with the National Health

Service which was, itself, increasingly coming to appreciate the importance of hospice work. Cancer Relief undertook to help build and equip a twenty-five-bed unit in the grounds of Christchurch Hospital in Dorset, in return for which the NHS agreed to take over complete responsibility for running and maintaining the unit when it was finished in 1975.

A year later the King Edward VII hospital at Midhurst in West Sussex offered a variation on the theme by setting up a new type of 'Macmillan unit' (the name Cancer Relief gave to such projects), using four or five of their *existing* hospital beds; the Macmillan staff based there began to undertake home visits. The scheme, which quickly spread to cover patients living up to twenty-five miles away, was funded jointly by the hospital and the charity. That was just one of the projects (St Christopher's had another in 1967) which sowed the seeds of a partnership between the hospice charities and local health authorities or government which continues in varying degrees around the country to this day.

As the number of hospices grew, as experiences were shared and lessons learnt, it became clear that, wherever possible, the best way to look after cancer patients was in their own homes. The patients themselves preferred it; it was, in most cases, much more cost-effective; and it greatly increased the hospice's 'reach' within the community. So, like St Christopher's and, later, St Joseph's, many hospices began to develop their own home-care teams, complementing the in-patient facilities on offer. It was an inevitable step in hospice development – completing the great circle of caring.

Many, but not all, hospices now have home-care teams. In some areas where hospices have been slow to get off the ground the home-care teams have arrived first, operating on their own – and, in some cases, helping to create the impetus for building a day-care centre or hospice proper. Cancer Relief's Macmillan Nurses are one such group – celebrating their 500th nurse in 1988 – and, again, they are the product of a deal with the government. The charity pays for the nurses' training and the wages for their first three years in the job. At that point the charity's financing role ends and the National Health Service takes over. It works well – the charity makes an investment to prove the need for a nurse in a particular hospice or area and then the government starts picking up the bill, freeing the charity's money to train another nurse or fund one more area of hospice need. It is a measure of the growing importance of the role of the Macmillan nurses that the National Society for Cancer Relief has changed its named to 'Cancer Relief Macmillan Fund'.

But home-care teams have developed in other ways as well: Tunbridge Wells in Kent has its own independent local charity, 'Hospice at Home', with nurses on call twenty-four hours a day, seven days a week. Their money now comes from their own fund-raising efforts within the community they serve, along with very substantial help from the local health authority.

The Marie Curie provide 4600 part-time nurses, almost nation-wide, to look after cancer patients for full shifts throughout the day or night when the pressure on relatives or carers becomes too great. Marie Curie nurses are given their work by the local health authority, which pays for half their cost. This service can be requested by the GP, community nurse, Macmillan nurse or even the patient.

Some NHS hospitals have not been slow to develop their own version of home care. In 1977 an NHS symptom-control team working from St Bartholomew's Hospital in Rochester began to provide advice on the control of symptoms, help in the patient's own home and support for the family. On that team were a consultant/general surgeon, a nursing office/co-ordinator, two nursing sisters, a social worker, chaplain and a clerical assistant. In that same year another NHS hospital support team was established at St Thomas's in London. By 1989 there were about twenty such teams in the UK, bringing to acute hospitals the hospice approach – and the hospice message.

But in many ways that message was just scratching the surface of medical opinion.

As recently as 1978, a study by Dr Colin Murray Parkes showed that, despite important advances over the previous decade, over a quarter of cancer patients dying in hospital and a fifth of those dying at home were in severe, unrelieved pain; other common symptoms such as nausea, breathlessness and constipation were often not relieved as well as they might be. Something had to be done, on top of all the hospices' other commitments, to educate others within the medical profession – to spread the word, to convince many more doctors and nurses about the vital importance of hospice work. The main hospice charities continued to respond to that challenge through the 1980s, their voices strengthened by the slowly growing public awareness of their work. And so, in November 1987, the Royal College of Physicians recognized terminal care as 'a new sub-speciality of general internal medicine' and opted for the already established name – *palliative medicine*. Soon afterwards the Joint Committee on Higher Medical Training approved a training programme in palliative medicine for senior registrars. And when, in 1987, the government asked all health authorities to review their services for the terminally ill, many responded by asking for more doctors trained in palliative medicine. Other developments included a regular *Journal of Palliative Medicine*, which first appeared in 1987, and the formation in 1985 of the Association of Palliative Care and Hospice Doctors of Great Britain and Ireland (now re-named Association for Palliative Medicine). After three years this had 205 members, including sixty-six full-time consultants or medical directors. Eleven of its members were in full or part-time academic posts in palliative medicine, nine of them funded by Cancer Relief for up to five years. You could say 'message received and understood' – but most experts believe there is still an enormous task ahead in spreading the gospel about palliative care. Substantial areas of the NHS are only just beginning to learn from the outstanding experience of the hospices in practising, evaluating and teaching pain control.

It was during the 1980s that the hospice movement gained another national voice. The 'Help the Hospices' charity was founded by the Duchess of Norfolk in 1984, with the strong backing of respected hospice figures such as Dame Cicely Saunders, Profess Eric Wilkes and the BMA's Professor Peter Quilliam. They argued that, despite the best will in the world, the existing hospice charities could not do everything – the hospice movement was now simply too big for that – and some areas of, in the main, short-term hospice need were slipping through the net. Needless to say, some of the other charities were not exactly enamoured by that particular diagnosis or its proposed cure – another charity. But they warmed somewhat towards the new arrival when they realized that it was an extra forum for creating public awareness and for internal debate, and was generally singing the same song. It did, indeed, help hospices to cross a few more items off their shopping lists – and even delighted some of the other charities by offering to fund projects that were close to their particular hearts. But, above all, it gave a new focus to the growing view that the hospice movement had to win the hearts and minds of more key players in the medical profession and that a steady drip-feed of money was necessary to do that.

Help the Hospices chose to concentrate on smaller, short-term projects – courses in counselling, business-management courses for medical staff, seminars on the vexed question of social security benefits for dying patients (they have to wait six months before they can claim an attendance allowance), and a Medical Fellowship scheme funding NHS doctors, without hospice experience, for crash courses in palliative care. These schemes, in the end, were indeed seen to fill in some of the 'gaps', fitting neatly around the plans of the other charities which were already up and running with longer-term educational developments.

The Marie Curie Memorial Foundation had, meanwhile, established an education department offering multi-disciplinary conferences and courses throughout the UK, covering all aspects of cancer care. And they were pouring money into their Research Institute in Surrey in a bid to develop new ways of tackling specific cancer conditions.

Cancer Relief was working to establish a network of nurse tutors and a small number of nursing lectureships – not to mention the steady lobbying (by example) of medical and nursing communities by the growing number of Macmillan nurses working amongst them. But it was recognized that still more needed to be done and, by 1989, Cancer Relief was arguing powerfully that ways had to be found to inject deeper into the NHS the proven palliative care skills and general philosophy of the hospice movement. They were even talking of establishing a university Chair in Palliative Medicine in the early 1990s.

More immediately, the human targets for persuasion in mid-1989 were, quite simply, anyone likely to come into contact with cancer patients, such as social workers, physiotherapists, occupational therapists and chaplains – but, above all, doctors, whose impact on the standards of palliative care was seen as crucial. *The Hospice Handbook* survey asked hospices and home-care teams to say whether their local GPs were either supportive, hostile or 'coming round'. Only four services reported that their GPs were hostile; fifty-five said they were 'coming round'; twenty said they were divided between 'coming round and supportive'; and an overwhelming 144 said they were supportive. So great progress is being made on the family doctor front, although there is still much to do in other areas.

Circling around the major hospice charities like a host of attentive satellites are some seventy other charities and organizations, each concentrating on a particular area of need and spread across Britain from Glasgow to the Isle of Wight.

To take just a few: trained cancer nurses are but a telephone call away – waiting in the offices of BACUP to offer emotional support and practical advice to newly diagnosed patients. Volunteers who have had breast cancer back up the staff at the Breast Care and Mastectomy Association of Great Britain. If you have been told you have any type of cancer and just need to talk about it, CancerLink has over 300 support and self-help groups around the country; Care offer fifty more. Perhaps you have lost a son or daughter: a group of parents who have been through that experience are waiting with personal or group support. They call themselves The Compassionate Friends. And if you have to cope with facial disfigurement after an operation, Let's Face It offers a link with people who have had a similar experience. Did you know that if your child has cancer, you can get cash grants to help with clothing, equipment, travel and fuel bills by applying to the Malcolm Sargent Cancer Fund for Children? Details of those and many more charities ready and waiting to help, can be found in the Hospice Charities chapter later in this book (see pp. 87–107).

What it all adds up to is that the hospice movement is striding into the nineties with a professionalism, vigour and clarity of purpose that pays great tribute to its many dedicated workers and unpaid volunteers. As a pressure group it is deliberately non-political, aware that its best interests are served by lobbying and arguing its financial case quietly behind the scenes with the government of the day, whatever its political hue; and it is realistic enough to know that, however much the government gives, there will always be a strong dependence on charitable giving to pay for all its requirements as it reaches for ever-new uplands of excellence. It can point with pride to a track record that has seen a modest twelve in-patient hospice units in the late sixties grow by mid-1989 to 133, offering over 3000 beds and caring for 40,000 people every year; it can record that, while thirty-three hospices are run by the National Health Service, 100 are independent charitable organizations and there are some thirty more hospices in the planning pipeline; and its 250 home-care teams and 4600 night nurses chart the path to the hospice movement of the twenty-first century.

3. INSIDE A HOSPICE
The Patient's View

Most patients arriving at a hospice for the first time are inevitably filled with a certain amount of apprehension. The have only vaguely heard of hospices before, probably in connection with someone they did not know, and perhaps in an 'over-the-garden-fence' conversation with a neighbour, when the natural sadness of the patient's circumstances became a part of the image of the place that patient was going to. Is not a hospice, they might wonder, a place to fear because of its association with death? Well – let's clear the air about that! Fear of hospices is an unfortunate hang-up of history – a by-product of old wives' tales and ill-informed gossip. It is also an inevitable consequence of being brought up in a nation that, on the whole, prefers not to think about death and refuses to discuss it in any terms except hushed whispers and much shaking of heads.

And yet, dying is the one great certainty of our lives. How ridiculous that, until comparatively recently, most of the British media regarded it as forbidden territory – 'not exactly the kind of subject matter that the readers or viewers want to hear about'. And yet it concerns us all. We should accept the possible approach of death, if not without fear then at least with a greater understanding of what is involved for patients and their families during the last days, weeks or months of life. And hospices are the beacons that light the way to that understanding. They are built around the simple maxim that a patient *really lives* until the very moment he or she dies – and that means making their lives as full of hope, happiness, comfort and caring as is humanly possible. And that is why the lasting impression – the one feeling that shines through from the patients in any hospice you care to visit – is one of gratitude, of sheer thankfulness that they have been fortunate to 'discover' a place such as this.

When I met Ivan he was sixty, dying of asbestosis. After more than six months in a general hospital, he had been brought to a hospice by his sister Marjorie and her family. 'It's not like a hospital,' he told me. 'They've got time for you here. They're looking after me really well – you just couldn't beat this.' And his sister agreed – 'It's absolutely marvellous! He's only been here a week and they've already started helping him so much. He can get out of bed in the morning and stand for a few seconds and he couldn't do that before.'

Joseph came to a hospice after doctors gave him just a few days to live. He just could not believe that such places existed. 'I'd heard about the hospice for a long, long time, but it never really sank in until I came here. It's beautiful – really nice.'

Ivy had confounded her doctors and become almost a permanent fixture in her hospice. Her verdict: 'I'm very happy here. I couldn't be in a better place, and all my relatives agree.'

And that's the remarkable thing about hospices – everybody who has experienced them *does* agree that there is a universal quality of care, a feeling of well-being which, given some of the circumstances, is quite extraordinary. Nurses go out of their way to get to know their patients, to become involved with them and their relatives. And around every hospice you will find a small army of dedicated volunteers, drawn from all sections of the neighbouring community. You do not have to be religious to appreciate and admire the sheer goodness that seems to radiate from the walls of these very special places. The Archbishop of Canterbury, Dr Robert Runcie, summed up the wider reach of the hospice movement:

I regard it as one of the best things that has happened as a reflection of idealism in British society since the war. I've seen and visited a number of hospices and, in every case, I found them unbelievable places of serenity and hope – and also, what I have noticed again and again, are the ripples that the creation of a hospice make in the total community, because so many people are in on it from voluntary helpers to nurses and those who simply go in with the newspapers. The patients are, of course, the centre of it all, but they're not doing something for themselves and it's not something being done to them – it's something rather special that's happening that is giving hope in society.

4. DAY HOSPICES

The hospice movement has long appreciated that there are many patients with cancer or other life-threatening illnesses who neither need nor want the round-the-clock care that comes with being resident in a hospice. They prefer to live at home, looked after by relatives, perhaps with friendly neighbours dropping in or keeping a watchful eye. But such carers need and deserve time off – either because they have work to go to, shopping to do, or they just need a break. That is where *day* hospices play such a vital role, offering patients a day away from home in comfortable, caring and warm surroundings – and relatives the freedom to do as they please.

Although many hospices have day centres, some do not – usually because the funding is not yet there. A few rural areas do not – and will not – have day centres because their relative remoteness makes access too difficult and journeys too time-consuming for patients, staff and volunteers. Conversely, day centres are starting to spring up in areas that do not have an in-patient hospice; many operate very effectively on their own but the people running such 'stand-alone' day centres almost all say they regard them as 'stepping stones' to a hospice proper.

How to Qualify for a Day Centre

As with all hospice services, a patient first has to be referred for day care by their own doctor or by a member of a home-care team (see next chapter) working closely with the local GP. A member of the day centre's nursing staff will then assess and admit those patients it is felt will benefit from a day spent away from home. Such patients might include those who have been discharged from in-patient care in a hospice and those who have been discharged from a hospital and find this a useful halfway house for getting used to the idea of terminal care.

There is no charge for patients; all services are free – although you will become aware, as one day centre put it, that 'donations are always welcome to help us expand and improve the services for both existing patients and new ones'.

A Typical Day

A typical day might begin with the relative personally delivering the patient to the day centre; or, if that is not possible, there are usually private car, ambulance or mini-bus 'collection' services manned by volunteers or local health-authority staff. The mini-buses might be donated by local business organizations such as Rotary, the Lions and the Women's Institute; they might be given by local or national charities; or they could be provided by the local council or health authority. Almost certainly there will be one available that accommodates wheelchairs.

The patients arrive into a world that offers almost everything they could want – from coffee to conversation, from meals to manicures. The emphasis is on providing an informal, relaxed family day. Staff and volunteers work together to provide a secure and warm atmosphere for patients where problems can be discussed, troubles shared, friendships made and confidence built. And, of course, the hospice's in-patients are also most welcome.

On offer at the day centre will be a combination of, if not all, the following services:

specialist nursing care;
pain and symptom control;
medical advice – visits by hospice doctor;
counselling;
physiotherapy;
occupational therapy – light and creative physical activities designed to stimulate patients mentally e.g., painting, weaving, pottery;
reassurance and support for patients and relatives;
hairdressing and beauty salon;
spacious lounge, Snug and 'Quiet' room;
superbly equipped bathroom with all modern facilities;
sun lounge;
well-equipped kitchen and dining facilities;
colour television;
treatment room;
pleasant garden.

And, just in case you think it highly unlikely that any day centre could offer absolutely *everything* on the above list, let me tell you one in Teesside comes very close. Purpose-built as almost all the new day centres are, it is by no means untypical of this important type of hospice facility. You can judge the atmosphere by their boast that they can call on no fewer than 250 trained volunteers to help the highly qualified nurses and other full-time staff. So, more often than not, attention is given on a one-to-one basis for much of the day – ensuring that besides everything else on offer, nobody goes short of a good chat! And the spirit of day centres is summed up best by two splendid paragraphs of promise at the end of the Teesside appeals brochure:

Patients can spend their day having a hairdo or a luxurious jacuzzi . . . or simply sharing the companionship of others at the Centre. A mid-day appetizer is followed by a delicious hot lunch with further opportunities to enjoy the Centre's facilities during the afternoon. Birthdays and anniversaries are always opportunities to join in a celebration tea before being driven back home later by a volunteer.

Time and again you hear patients and relatives pay tribute to hospices for offering 'the personal touch that busy hospitals simply don't have time for'. And to people with long-term and life-threatening illnesses, that personal touch, that collective family embrace, is what makes all the difference.

5. HOSPICE HELP IN YOUR OWN HOME

Despite the great range of help available in hospices and day centres, there is no doubt that the vast majority of patients with cancer or other life-threatening illnesses would prefer to be looked after in their own homes. All the care and attention in the world cannot duplicate the therapeutic familiarity of one's own surroundings. Hence the clear need for a skilled professional service directly aimed at preventing distress and anxiety in both patients and relatives living with them. The hospice movement has responded to this need with *home-care* teams – highly qualified nurses on call to undertake regular visits and respond to telephone requests for help. Almost 100 hospices have home-care teams – and that includes most of the hospice units in NHS hospitals. But some 200 home-care teams operate in areas that do not yet have hospices. There is general agreement that one major way forward for the hospice movement in the nineties is through the development of home care.

It must be said that, in the early days, many local GPs viewed the home-care nurses with a degree of suspicion – saw them as muscling in on their patch and even, it was occasionally murmured, disturbing the delicate relationship of trust between doctor and patient. That latent and irrational hostility still rumbles on in a few areas – but, by the end of the 1980s, most GPs were steadily coming round and appreciating the extra degree of help these nurses could give and the reliability of their medical and emotional back-up. In return the hospice movement is at pains to stress that their nurses, doctors and the rest of the team are an *extra* resource at the disposal of the often hard-pressed GP, and are *not* a bid to take over his job. They undertake to work closely with him and the primary health-care team. And, of course, the call summoning hospice help of whatever kind invariably comes – *has* to come – either from the GP himself or from the district nurse.

Who Provides the Home Care Nursing Teams?

Home-care nurses come largely, in the first instance, from two main charitable sources – Cancer Relief Macmillan Fund and The Marie Curie Community Nursing Service. Both consider this work of crucial future importance and are stepping up their funding of it accordingly. Cancer Relief has even given itself a new public title, 'Cancer Relief *Macmillan* Fund', to reflect better the main thrust of its work. The fund has the government's backing for a pump-priming partnership in the home-care field. It takes experienced community nurses, pays for them to have additional specialist training in terminal care and their salaries for their first three years in the job. Then the Health Service steps in to take over the funding. A surge in development in the late eighties saw the number of Macmillan nurses top the 500 mark with care being provided for 50,000 patients a year. And almost every month more are coming on stream, taking their techniques of pain control and the skills needed to provide emotional support right to the patient's own living room. And it should be stressed that they are part of a team, working closely with the GPs and local nurses but, because of the specific nature of their appointment, they do not shoulder the full range of medical duties and so can offer unhurried support to patients and their relatives. Cancer Relief acknowledges that the district or community nurse remains, at all times, the primary nurse, however great the involvement of her Macmillan colleague.

You will find a Macmillan nurse on many home-care teams – but there are other home-care operations unconnected with Cancer Relief that offer a similar service. Some are NHS in-patient units e.g., in Brighton, and some are independent hospices e.g., in Dartford, doing this home-care work to a high standard in their own way and with their own funding.

The Marie Curie Memorial Foundation started their home nursing in the wake of their 1952 report and, by the end of the eighties, their Community Nursing Service had some 4600 nurses looking after more than 14,000 patients for a total of over half a million hours a year. Most Marie Curie nurses are Registered General Nurses or Enrolled Nurses; some are experienced nursing auxiliaries. Many are young mothers with family commitments who wish to continue nursing, but only on a part-time basis. They are, in general, jointly funded by the National Health Service and administered by local health authorities. They can be available at any time but specialize in night nursing to enable those caring for a loved one at home to obtain adequate rest. Community nursing officers will tell you how to apply for such nursing care.

The Marie Curie and Macmillan nurses concentrate almost exclusively on cancer cases – but such is the success of home-care operations and their adoption by the hospice movement and a growing number of hospitals, that some home-care teams willingly embrace patients in the advanced stages of other severely debilitating or life-threatening illnesses, such as muscular dystrophy, multiple sclerosis, motor-neurone disease and, increasingly, AIDS.

The Sue Ryder Foundation works with patients who have a wide range of disabilities. Some of their eighty homes in Britain and overseas (seven of them UK cancer hospices) have visiting nurses who attend patients in their own homes, both before admission and after discharge. Referral to a Sue Ryder home is usually through the patient's doctor, social worker or radiotherapy centre.

Whoever organizes it, home care invariably brings great relief and comfort to those it is intended to help. Kathleen, who was in her sixties and had cancer, wanted to stay in her own home. She told me what a home-care team meant to her: 'Whenever you want them – it doesn't matter what time of night, or any time – you've only got to pick up the telephone and they'll be here. And the hospice gave me the telephone because I wasn't connected before.' She had discovered another way in which they were prepared to help: 'I was going on holiday and an envelope came; I thought it was a card to say "Have a nice holiday," and there was £30 spending money in the envelope. Wasn't that kind of them?'

Then there was Sandy – when I met her she was in the middle of a long and brave fight with cancer of the bowel. Her local home-care team had provided, on permanent loan, a machine which greatly eased her pain. With remarkable coolness, she said,

'With this disease there's a lot of fear, and I think the home-care team have eradicated that. With the least little worry, you can ring them and they'll be here instantly. It can be a pain problem or a dietary problem or any sort of problem – just a silly little fear – and they'll come and calm you down again, give you very practical advice and also help all the family, the children as well. Any equipment we are given by the home-care team is ours for as long as we need it, and if I had to rely on the NHS and go to the local hospital I would only receive about three hours' treatment a week whereas, with a machine at home, I use it nearly four hours every day.'

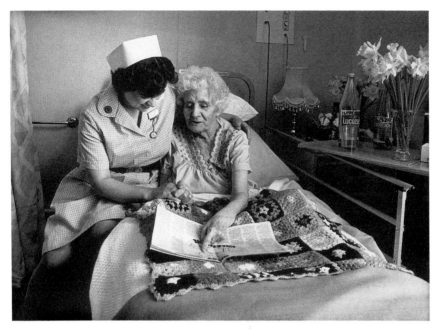

Mrs Ivy Thomas and a nurse at Nightingale Macmillan Continuing Care unit at Derby.

Counselling an AIDS patient.

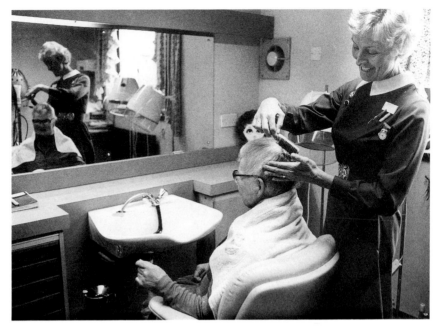

Mrs E. Neal at Michael Sobell House, Mount Vernon Hospital,
Northwood, Middlesex.

Day Unit scene from left to right: Elsie Sneath, Merlin (volunteer),
and Jack Thompson.

6. HELP FOR RELATIVES
Bereavement Counselling

The help that a hospice offers is rarely limited to the patient alone, but reaches out to embrace relatives too. Right from the very early days of the hospice movement there has been concern for those people sitting at the bedside – and much thought about how they will live with themselves when they can no longer live with their loved one; that is where specially trained volunteers, known as bereavement counsellors, come in. Very often their work starts well before a bereavement, preparing people to face the inevitable loss. And then afterwards they are a strong, firm shoulder to lean on, understanding the moods, the emotions, the pain, the anger and the anxieties that can ebb and flow for months, and possibly years, afterwards. Many such counsellors will have suffered a loss themselves; they will know and understand only too well what people are going through; and to that understanding they will add the knowledge gained from considerable and careful training. They will have discussed in great depth the whole psychology of people's reactions and will understand that grief, like the individuals it affects, cannot be slotted into predictable compartments. Above all, they will be good listeners who will recognize those moments when words are inadequate or inappropriate.

Elisabeth Earnshaw-Smith, Director of Social Work at St Christopher's Hospice in south-east London, has written the definitive guide to such a service. It must, she writes, be seen to be building a bridge for the future. And she emphasizes the special role of the counsellors

and all they bring with them of satisfying relationships and life experience, of tried ways of handling disappointments, crises and losses in themselves, their families and friends. They also bring with them optimism, a belief that there is a way through, together with all the individual qualities for which they have been selected.

Such counsellors quickly learn how to recognize, and help deal with, the many different and difficult ways in which grief is expressed, such as the bereaved person who is withdrawn and finds it hard to speak, the person who can't stop talking, the person who fears that once they cry they will not be able to stop, the person with suicidal thoughts or the person who has resorted to drink to blot out his or her pain and sorrow.

The moment when a bereavement counsellor is first needed can vary and hospices are good at recognizing that moment of need and offering help. If there are no family or friends actually present at the time of death, contact is usually made quickly – perhaps even accompanying the bereaved person to their home and helping them settle down for the night. Then they may need help through the inevitable formalities – the visits to the registrar, the funeral director and perhaps the funeral itself.

But when there are family and friends around, the bereavement counsellor will delay visiting in order to encourage family members to take responsibility for each other, thus increasing family cohesion. Help may be most needed one to three months after the death, when neighbours and family are withdrawing and beginning to expect the bereaved to be 'normal'. That can be the loneliest time when old memories come flooding back.

It goes without saying that counsellors will never force themselves on the bereaved. Fine judgements have to be made as to the greatest moment of need and the right approach. There is no point in seeing the next-of-kin alone if that is going to risk splitting a potentially supportive relationship; and it is little help seeing a family together when some of them prefer not to share their thoughts so widely. Some people become so depressed they withdraw into themselves, often rejecting help when it is most needed; others will know when they need help most, and actively seek it, keeping close at hand the counsellor's name and telephone numbers for a call that may come within days, months or even, in some cases, years. Bereavement counsellors have to be ready and able to deal with all kinds of reaction at all times.

Naturally, many bereaved people develop a strong bond with the hospice where someone important to them lived their last days and then died in peace. They regard the staff and the volunteer counsellors as friends and return to visit them at mutually convenient moments. Doctors and nurses often go out of their way to talk because they accept that such contact is part of the hospice tradition; long-lasting friendships can develop.

One hospice organizer who has regular church services and get-togethers for the bereaved every two months described the

very special people who volunteer to become bereavement
counsellors:

The volunteers are important to us: the bereaved could not be visited so
thoroughly and in such numbers without them, and the services could not
take place without them as they chauffeur people, swell the singing,
serve the tea and, most importantly, sit and talk. They are generous with
their time and with their skills and they are courageous – it does take
courage to approach someone who might tell you to go away or burst into
tears.

Elisabeth Earnshaw-Smith sums it up well: 'A bereavement
service in a community stands for the recognition of the pain of
loss, for the necessity of grieving and for the possibility of using
the experience to start living in a new way.' And she lists no fewer
than twenty separate factors which can complicate a bereavement
and which counsellors might have to take into account. They are
worth repeating here to help the layman identify factors which he
or she may not recognize as possible complications preventing an
overcoming of grief:

1. children or adolescents in the immediate family;
2. dependent family members (handicapped, elderly, sick);
3. loss of primary care giver/constant companion/emotional
   support;
4. loss of financial provision;
5. loss of home – feared or actual;
6. anxiety about making decisions;
7. family unable to share feelings;
8. reluctance to face facts of illness or death;
9. marital or family discord;
10. communication difficulties in the family;
11. memories of uncontrolled pain, emotional distress or nursing
    difficulties during the loved one's illness;
12. presence of concurrent life crises;
13. difficulty in dealing with previous losses;
14. excessive or prolonged emotional reaction/mental illness/
    suicidal thoughts;
15. lack of spiritual support;
16. lack of community support;
17. self-care difficulties;
18. distress over changed body image or personality of loved one
    before death;

19. absence at time of death; did not say goodbye; did not attend funeral;
20. (more obviously) violent death or suicide.

These twenty factors led to Help the Hospices training over 100 hospice personnel in family management skills, with the help of the Institute of Family Therapy.

The best ways of helping the bereaved vary from person to person; but one of the best sets of general guidelines comes from Pam Bemmett, who has experienced the loss of three close members of her family, two of them through cancer.

This is her advice, which is commended by CRUSE, BACUP, MARIE CURIE and CANCER RELIEF, amongst others.

Offering comfort

BY PAM BENNETT

After the death of my husband Lawrie, I put together a few do's and don't's based on my own experiences, to help the many thousands of kind, caring people who tell the recently bereaved: 'I just don't know what to say to you.'

DO make telephone calls to them for a quick chat ('How are things going with you today?') or to invite them round for tea or coffee, even those you don't know very well. But, this is very important, don't be hurt if they don't immediately take up your offer.

There were at least ten people in my village who said: 'Ring or pop in anytime, don't be alone.' I didn't ring very often or pop in, but the knowledge that they were there was sustaining and I shall never forget their thoughtfulness.

DO remember that because you may have found your bereaved friend out or occupied on the day you chose to call, it does not mean that they will be out or occupied every time you do so.

I was sometimes out when friends popped round, but I was also there alone for days on end. Curiously, at my lowest ebb, I did not make many calls myself for fear of spoiling another's day with my sadness. This was in spite of being told to do just that. Kindness abounds.

DO remember that very few people hate to be touched. A hand held even briefly when meeting or a quick hug can bring an enormous amount of warmth without words.

You can't really go about hugging comparative strangers, but a hand laid gently on the arm and saying, 'I'm so sorry to hear your news' or 'I've been thinking of you so much,' are positive statements which need no reply but a returned pressure of hands and a 'thank you', which is about all that can be managed at first without tears. It is perhaps wiser not to say: 'Please let me know if I can be of any help' unless you really do mean it. You might find yourself in a bit of a fix if taken at your word when you were just trying to console.

DO talk about the dear departed! One of the most hurtful experiences for me was if people avoided mentioning my husband's name. It was as if, to them, he had never existed. The reason for their silence, of course, was that they didn't want to distress me, but I yearned to hear his name on another's lips.

It was strange that some close friends were the ones mistakenly being tactful about this, whereas many of my acquaintances had no problems with the subject at all. At a dinner table where an argument had reached an impasse, one of the participants turned to me and said fiercely: 'Lawrie would have agreed with me, wouldn't he?' I told her he most certainly would have – it was so natural and such a joy to have him brought back, if only for a few seconds.

On another occasion, a neighbour of my mother, who lives by the sea, asked me how I was getting along. I was very moved when she added: 'I will never forget him ambling along with his camera over his shoulder. He was always so happy here.'

It is just as important to try not to be embarrassed by the mention of the departed's name by the bereaved, for 'To live in the hearts of those we love, is not to die.' This means allowing the bereaved to talk about their lost loved one, with or without tears, recalling past happiness, arguments or laughter.

DO tell someone who has been bereaved that you think of them. You would probably be surprised how much warmth comes from this, especially when months have passed. It is very comforting to know that someone really means what they say and wishes you peace of mind.

However, don't, if you can avoid it, ask 'How are you?' It is the most instinctive and well-intentioned question and nearly every-one asks it. Unfortunately, the bereaved person usually feels obliged to reply 'fine, fine', when they really want to say 'I can't bear it,' or they say 'OK,' when they mean 'I just can't believe it.'

My greatest comfort came from those who just put their arms around me and hugged me, saying very little. Their warmth and sincerity came through without words.

Please don't, if you wish to be a true comforter, tell the recently bereaved how lucky they are, for if there is one thing they do not feel, it is lucky. They know they are lucky perhaps to have their children, parents or home. Lucky to have no money worries, their health, a good marriage. Lucky to have friends, to be alive, to have a pension. They probably are lucky, but they don't want to be told that right away.

They are trying to come to terms with a great loss and can generally do without well-intentioned exhortations to 'look on the bright side'. So try not to say to your friend a few days after the funeral: 'How lucky you are to have had him.' If you can see that the relationship was good, then the loss is tremendous, the wound deep and it is too soon to feel 'lucky'. Curiously, if you do not point out the silver linings, it enables the bereaved, in time, to find them themselves and to be able to say 'How lucky I've been.'

It can be just as hurtful to make comparisons. In my experience, it did not help me to bear the pain when I was told that there were others worse off than myself. I knew that there were and that they were probably much braver. Within days of my husband's death I had been told, though not by them, that I was much better off than two widows of my acquaintance whose husbands had died many years previously. I knew how fortunate I was to have two devoted children, a fond mother and true friends and certainly I was much more fortunate than anyone on their own, but that did not lessen my grief. When you have lost someone close, only you know how much this means to you and comparisons can only wound.

On a similar note, if there is anything seemingly calculated to depress the bereaved, it is being 'jollied'. 'Never mind,' said some well-meaning friends, 'you'll feel better when the baby comes.' At the time it seemed a curious exchange to me – the warmth of a husband and lover, for that of a baby, my first grandchild.

'Never mind,' said the same people when five months later the little baby and his parents had to go and live in the Far East for three years, 'you'll be able to look forward to the photos, letters and visiting them.' On the other hand, when people said: 'Oh no, what will you do now?' I was able to say: 'It isn't the end – thank goodness I can visit them,' and then talk about the wonderful new job that caused the move. 'Oh no, just when the baby's arrived' allowed me to say: 'I just can't believe it – thank goodness it's only for three years.'

Of course, the jolly friends were right in the end. The little baby sleeping on my breast did bring renewed strength and warmth, something to be cherished. They just had the timing a bit wrong! So don't be jolly at first, because strangely enough when you are not, it allows the bereaved to show a bit of backbone.

A final few words of hope for those who are alone, for what is life without sharing? It means making yourself go out and trying to return home in a positive frame of mind to a silent house. It means doing your best to plan optimistically for the years ahead.

Nothing will be the same again. This has to be accepted finally and, with the help of friends and family, so generous with their love and caring, there will be happy times to help you bear this.

Further Information

There are many books and publications which the bereaved may find comforting and helpful to read. They include:

FICTION

A Death in the Family by J. Agee, pub. Peter Owen, 1965.
In the Springtime of the Year by S. Hill, pub. Hamish Hamilton, 1974.

NON-FICTION

The Bereaved Parent by H.S. Schiff, pub. Souvenir Press, 1979.
Children, Death and Bereavement by P. Wynne-Jones, pub. Scripture Union, 1985.
The Courage to Grieve by J. Tatelbaum, pub. Heinemann, 1981.
Death and the Family by L. Pincus, pub. Faber & Faber, 1976 (specially recommended)
A Grief Observed by C.S. Lewis, pub. Faber & Faber, 1961.
Helping Children Cope with Separation and Loss by C. Jewett, pub. British Agencies for Adoption & Fostering, 1984.
Learning to Say Goodbye: When a Parent Dies by E. Leshan, pub. Avon Books, 1978.
Letting Go – Caring for the Dying and the Bereaved by I. Ainsworth-smith & P. Speck, pub. SPCK, 1982.
Losses: Talking about Bereavement by R. Richardson, pub. Open Books, 1980.
On Children and Death by E. Kubler-Ross, pub. Macmillan Publishing Co (New York), 1983.

Psychological Therapy for Patients with Cancer by Stirling Moorey & Steven Greer, pub. Heinemann Medical Books, 1989.

Talking about Death: a Dialogue between Parent and Child by E.A. Grollman, pub. Beacon Press (Boston), 1976.

When Your Loved One is Dying by E.A. Grollman, pub. Beacon Press (Boston), 1980.

A more detailed list can be obtained from the Hospice Information Service at St Christopher's Hospice, 51-9 Lawrie Park Road, Sydenham, London SE26 6DZ. Tel. 01 778 9252. They are fully up-to-date with all hospice bereavement services round the country (and all other developments in the hospice movement too). There is also a specialized bookselling service covering all aspects of care of the dying, bereavement, grief, counselling and cancer care nursing for patients, families and professionals. It is called Meditec and it issues an updated stock list several times a year (free on request). All UK orders are sent post free. The address is Meditec, Tork House, 26 Bourne Road, Colsterworth, Lincs. NG33 5JE. Tel. 0476 860281. Although most hospices are aiming to provide their own bereavement counselling service, some do not yet do so. But there are two organizations that specialize in offering strong back-up in this sensitive area.

CRUSE is an established national network which helps *any* bereaved person by providing counselling individually or in groups by trained counsellors. It offers advice and information on practical problems and social contact; it also provides training courses for professionals and counsellors. The address is Cruse House, 126 Sheen Road, Richmond, Surrey TW9 1UR. Tel. 01 940 4818.

The Compassionate Friends is a self-help group of parents who have lost a son or daughter of *any* age. Their emphasis is on befriending rather than counselling. They offer a quarterly newsletter, a postal library, a range of leaflets and both personal and group support. You will find them at 6 Denmark Street, Bristol, BS1 5DQ. Tel. 0272 292778.

The National Association of Bereavement Services is building up a register of all bereavement services in the United Kingdom. They can be contacted c/o London VSC, 68 Chalton Street, London NW1 1JR. Tel. 01 388 2153.

There is now no reason why anyone who has been bereaved should lack proper help from people who understand fully the kind of emotional pressures they are under and can draw on a wide range of experience in working out the best way to help.

7. AIDS AND THE HOSPICE MOVEMENT

The hospice movement is characterized by an extraordinary degree of hope and friendship. But there are times when it has to be acknowledged that hope has largely gone – and that is when the friendship, support and quality of care provided by hospices comes into their own. The aim then is to ensure that a person *really lives* until the very moment they die – that has long been enshrined in hospice philosophy. This aim has found a new purpose – and some new problems – in the arrival during the 1980s of the HIV disease known as AIDS. This insidious virus has rapidly established itself in almost 150 countries. It can be carried in the body for years before developing into AIDS proper, a condition for which there is no known cure. The World Health Organization, in a bleak report published in May 1989, predicted a massive surge in infections over the following five years. Its team of experts forecast that, by the end of the century, almost twenty million people worldwide could be infected with the virus, with more than five million dead or dying from the disease. Up to the end of May 1989, Britain had reported 2296 cases, just under half of whom had died; but British government researches estimate that, by 1992, up to 30,000 people could have developed AIDS, taking the total AIDS death toll up to a possible 17,000 (Cox Report, HMSO, 1988). Experts, however, are at pains to stress that accurate predictions are impossible because there are too many unknown factors involved, such as the extent to which AIDS will spread through the heterosexual community.

Seen at first as 'the gay plague' for the way it appeared to strike exclusively at the homosexual community, the HIV virus now shows signs of spreading into other groups. An official British survey in March 1989 of all the full-blown cases of AIDS since the disease was first recorded here showed that 81 per cent were gay men, 2 per cent were drug addicts (using infected needles), 6 per cent were haemophiliacs and 4 per cent were infected through *heterosexual* contact. The last figure is more alarming than its size at first suggests. It refers, remember, to just full-blown cases –

and for each one of those there are many more carriers who do not even know the virus is in their bodies, poised to infect someone else. And there is another worrying complication too. Despite massive advertising campaigns it seems that young heterosexuals still don't regard AIDS as a problem affecting them, so they are not presenting themselves for testing in anything like the expected numbers. That, in itself, increases further the potential spread of the disease. But the biggest concern is caused by the smallest statistic – the 2 per cent who are drug addicts. The Health Minister, David Mellor, speaking at the end of May 1989 to a nineteen-nation conference examining AIDS and drug abuse in Europe, warned that the threat of a 'real AIDS epidemic spreading through the population of Britain' was in the balance; drug addicts infected with the HIV virus were, as he put it, the 'bridgehead into the heterosexual community' for spreading the disease generally. It is clear that, as time goes on, AIDS will be seen less and less as an exclusively 'gay' problem.

Fully understanding the spread of the virus has been delayed by strident early voices anxious to apportion blame, and feeding off fear and prejudice. (They did the same when syphilis struck an unsuspecting world in the fifteenth century; then, Britain blamed France and Russia blamed Poland!) But there comes a point in any humane society when arguing over who was to blame for the spread of the deadly disease has to take a black seat to caring for those who have got it; and, inevitably, the spotlight fell on the hospice movement with its expertise and powerful record of caring for the often terminally ill. In 1986, the then Health Secretary, Norman Fowler, said he thought hospices had a vital role to play in caring for people with AIDS: at first the hospices were not so sure!

Much debate ensued within the movement. Did not many hospices already have their hands full looking after *cancer* patients – with many more cancer cases on their waiting lists? Was it not more difficult to tell when AIDS patients entered a terminal phase? And did they not often require radical curative treatment which was not appropriate for hospices which are more concerned with *care*? Did not a large proportion of hospice funding come from charities or individuals who wished specifically to help the development of *cancer* care, and nothing else? Many covenants and legacies winging their way were conditional upon being used to help people suffering from *cancer*. Would some of that vital money move away if AIDS patients were to be taken on board? Some still felt there was a moral stigma attached to AIDS patients. How would present and future cancer patients react to the newcomers? Could the necessary medical precautions be guaranteed? It was an enormous new worry for a movement whose history was marked by continuous financial struggle. Inevitably, with so many autonomous bodies involved, each hospice and home-care team would have to discuss it and eventually come up with its own answer. It would take time. And time was what AIDS patients did not have.

If some hospices were unable or unwilling to take people with AIDS, then those people and the many others who wished to help them would have to build their own hospices. London Light-house, the first organization in Britain to set up counselling and volunteer services for the growing number of men and women living with HIV, ARC and AIDS, officially opened a residential and support centre in November 1988. Based in a £5 million, purpose-designed building in North Kensington, it is committed to providing the best possible care, support and facilities to enable people affected by AIDS to live well throughout their lives. Its range of integrated services include a social centre, counselling, health and education programmes, home support as well as respite, convalescent and terminal care. London Lighthouse also provides support to the partners, friends and families of people affected by AIDS, and runs training courses for statutory, private and voluntary organizations and for individuals concerned with AIDS-related issues.

People can be referred by their doctor, their hospital – or even, unusually, by themselves. The twenty-four-bed residential unit is staffed by thirty-seven trained nurses and offers a choice of single or multi-bedded rooms, each finished to an exceptionally high standard. It is more like a home than a hospital, with the emphasis on comfort and informality, creating a safe, supportive and non-institutionalized environment where the residents are in control. And there is not a uniform in sight. Each staff member is, in effect, a guest, and is there because he or she possesses the skills which can help each patient to be in charge of his or her own life. One resident said, 'People are prepared to do things the way *you're* happiest with them – not in the way *they're* happiest.' Patients can have visitors twenty-four hours a day and the furnishings include sofa beds for those who wish to stay overnight.

The day centre – they prefer to call it the 'Drop-in-Centre and Cafe' – is open seven days a week and provides a relaxed and informal meeting place for people with HIV, ARC and AIDS, as well as their partners, families and friends. Their home support service provides non-medical nursing care and support through a network of trained neighbourhood teams. By the middle of 1989, 200 volunteers were working with more than seventy patients in their own homes, offering a night-time care service under the name 'Nightlights'.

The dedication of everyone involved has made an enormous impression on London's senior hospital doctors and consultants. One of them, Anthony Pinching, Senior Lecturer in Clinical Immunology at St Mary's Hospital Medical School, wrote this –

Lighthouse will not stand alone in the management of people with AIDS, but will enmesh with existing hospitals and community agencies and other voluntary sector contributions. In addition, it will provide a focal point for this major aspect of care and a model resource for future developments to ensure that people with AIDS receive the very best care in settings that can properly service their many needs.

There is much about the establishment and operational methods of London Lighthouse – in particular their highly flexible method of working – that points the way for other areas of care. The House of Commons Social Services Committee praised them for 'pioneering a facility which could provide a model for such projects elsewhere, and which will save the NHS a great deal of money, but above all will provide the type of care people want.' The London Lighthouse is at 111-7 Lancaster Road, London W11 1QT. Tel. 01 792 1200. There is also a National AIDS Helpline – 0800 567123 – to which free calls can be made twenty-four hours a day.

The Lighthouse is not the only London hospice for people with AIDS. The Mildmay Mission Hospital, run by an independent Christian charity, opened its Elizabeth Hospice and Continuing Care Unit for AIDS patients in February 1988. Not as big or as comprehensive as the Lighthouse, it was, however, the first such residential unit of its kind in Europe. Its model of care differs from the Lighthouse in one important respect – the staff wear uniforms. Mildmay's early consumer research indicated that people who are ill often feel more secure when cared for by easily recognized professionals. The hospice has reported a 'continual demand' for its first nine individual rooms which are staffed by twenty-four fully trained nurses. The volunteers too are carefully screened and trained, and the interdisciplinary team includes physio and occupational therapists, a chaplain, doctors and counsellors. The Mildmay planners felt that in order to provide high quality professional care which could be properly evaluated, it would be necessary to have high staff ratios. Eight more rooms were added in August 1989, as well as a day centre. Counselling, including family therapy, with bereavement support and follow-up, is available; and a home-care service provides advice and appropriate back-up for those taking care of patients in their own homes. 'Frontliners', a self-help support group for people with AIDS has its East End office at Mildmay. An education centre is being rapidly developed, and this hospice has won wide recognition for the high standards of its seminars and other training initiatives. (The transcripts of the lectures – summing up the experiences and lessons of its first full year – have been gathered together in a book published by Help the Hospices.) The Mildmay staff are driven by the thought that 'as Christians we are challenged to ensure that we offer compassionate and highly professional care in an atmosphere of unconditional love'. Their address is Mildmay Mission Hospital, Hackney Road, London E2 7NA. Tel. 01 739 2331.

A few other hospices devoted exclusively to AIDS patients are planned – the Milestone House in Edinburgh, which had to overcome considerable early difficulties, is probably the most advanced. Responding to the requests of people with AIDS, it is built on the 'core and cluster' design principle, with four bungalows attached to a central core of nursing, living and support services. This design combines a high degree of privacy with quick and easy access to nursing help. Fitting Milestone House into the overall provision of health care for people with AIDS should be as straightforward as fitting the third piece of a four-piece jigsaw. It can accommodate twenty people in twelve single rooms and four double flatlets. Great care has been taken with what its backers call 'the delicate process of consultation and education with the local community'. Planning to open at the end of 1989, the charity helping to raise money for the project is Milestone Venture Trust, 64 Broughton Street, Edinburgh EH1 3SA. Tel. 031 557 6580.

And what of other hospices taking AIDS patients? By 1989 a

clear pattern was beginning to emerge. St Christopher's Hospice in south-east London has continued its pioneering role and called a series of conferences to examine the whole question of AIDS in detail. Other hospice charities have provided practical experience and further teaching to supplement NHS courses. But, for all the clouds on the horizon, AIDS is not yet a major hospice preoccupation. The great majority of cases live in, or near, London and relate more to their NHS units or to the special AIDS hospices. Outside London, quietly and unassumingly, hospices increasingly accept the occasional local cases when NHS colleagues refer them.

So just how far are Britain's hospices prepared to open their doors to AIDS patients? The survey specially commissioned in early 1989 for *The Hospice Handbook* revealed that, of the 160 or so existing and planned in-patient hospices, fifty will accept suitable AIDS patients; twenty-two will accept them *only* if they also have cancer; thirty-three will not accept them at all; and thirty-two are unsure or have not yet taken a policy decision.

Of the 250 or so home-care teams, ninety-four say they will look after AIDS patients; eighteen will take them only if they also have cancer; sixty-three will not accept AIDS patients; and forty-nine are still making up their minds.

Many of those who will not accept AIDS patients qualified their replies by saying that the service is already provided elsewhere in their area, or their facilities are not suitable, or they are fully stretched with cancer patients. And most of *them* would not take in potential hospice patients with conditions such as motor-neurone disease either. One or two were still frightened that taking in AIDS patients might affect their fund-raising, but this is clearly not as big a factor as it was earlier in the decade. The hospice movement, despite its limited resources and relatively small size, has signalled its willingness to shoulder its share of responsibility in caring for AIDS patients. As one nurse put it,

The whole of the hospice movement and the NHS should embrace AIDS across the board, just as they should embrace whatever virus nature is going to throw at the human race. If we are a caring profession, we should nurse whoever comes our way.

Hospices and home-care teams that had, by mid-1989, agreed to look after AIDS patients are noted in the detailed Hospice Directory at the end of this book.

8. HOSPICE HELP FOR CHILDREN

At least 50 per cent of children's cancers now respond to treatment, but the process of recovery can be slow and debilitating; where recovery is unlikely, medical advances often make it possible to control the disease for far longer than was possible in the past, giving children many more years of life than they might otherwise expect. Of those who *are* dying of cancer, relatively few will need a children's hospice because it is often possible for such children to be cared for at home. So, in contrast to adult hospices, only 17 per cent of those who go to children's hospices have cancer or leukaemia. The great majority suffer from other types of slowly progressive, life-threatening diseases. But, whatever the cause, looking after such children can place a long-term burden on their parents – and the need to ease that burden prompted a leading Anglican nun, Mother Frances, to set up Helen House in Oxford. The first children's hospice anywhere in the world, it grew from a deep personal experience.

Helen was a bright, lively, happy child until, at the age of two and half, she developed a brain tumour. An emergency operation removed the tumour but left Helen's brain severely and irreversibly damaged. She was unable to speak, sit up or control her movements. Although she seemed to be partly aware of her surroundings, it was impossible to discover how much she understood. Soon after the operation Mother Frances, who was a registered children's nurse, met Helen and her parents and a close friendship developed. To give the parents a break, Mother Frances often looked after Helen in her convent in Oxford – and the idea of Helen House, purpose-built in the convent grounds, was born.

Its aims are clearcut:

- It does *not* provide long-term care but is a place where children *and their families* can come to stay from time to time in the same way that most of us have occasional holidays or go to spend a weekend with friends.

- On offer are friendship, support and practical skills – the parents can do as little or as much as they like, stay in one of the special flats for relatives or take a much-needed holiday knowing that their child is in the very best of hands.
- Not just parents, but whole families are welcome too – brothers, sisters, occasionally grandparents. The more unexpected arrivals have included a much-loved dog, a terrapin and even a pet tarantula! Don't worry – the tarantula left some time ago!
- Helen House is small and homely. There are just eight rooms – one for each child. Parents can choose between sleeping in the same room as their child, or in family accommodation with two double bedrooms, a sitting room, kitchen and bathroom, providing comfort and complete privacy.
- A jacuzzi provides therapy and relaxation. There is a large and marvellously peaceful garden, and a playroom so stacked with toys that it makes every day seem like Christmas!
- They welcome children of any race or belief, and at any age from birth to sixteen; they sometimes manage to look after them beyond that age but cannot normally take anyone for the first time beyond sixteen.
- There is no clear catchment area – children come from all over the United Kingdom and Channel Islands.
- Most children accepted here have progressive, life-threatening illnesses such as muscular dystrophy, Batten's disease, mucopolysaccharidoses and malignant disease – to mention but a few.
- It is *not* normally possible to accept children with an illness or handicap which is not life-threatening.
- There is no charge.

Mother Frances explained it to me like this: 'The strain and the loneliness of having a very sick child can be very great, and we just wanted to offer an ordinary kind of friendship to people facing an extraordinary kind of grief.'

How Do You Arrange Your First Visit?

It does not matter who makes the initial inquiry. Once it is established that a child has a life-threatening illness and that the family would like to use Helen House, then all that is needed is the agreement of the child's doctor. The family usually makes an initial visit, either overnight or for part of a day, so they and the staff can get to know each other. Great emphasis is placed on learning as much as possible about the child's likes and dislikes and the ways by which parents have succeeded in making their child most comfortable and at ease.

What are the Staff Like?

Helen House is run by people whose common qualification is their love and concern for children. They include trained nurses, teachers, a nursery nurse, a social worker, a physiotherapist, a chaplain and some parents. The medical officer is a local GP. An administrator, a secretary, two sisters from All Saints Convent and a few volunteers complete the team. Everyone shares the household chores as well as the care of children and their families, and no one wears uniform. If a child's home is near enough to Helen House, the doctor or other professional who cares for him or her at home is welcome to continue to be involved at Helen House. I nearly forgot one other very important member of staff – an engaging black-and-white mongrel called Tish!

If and when the time comes for a child to die, they try to ensure that this happens with dignity, the child surrounded by the people he or she knows and loves best, whether at home or in Helen House. And the friendship and support does not end there, but continues for as many months or years as the family wishes.

Since opening in November 1982 Helen House has become a wellhead of goodness and gratitude. Two parents, whose child was cared for there, wrote this moving and eloquent message to those who might have doubts about taking a very sick child away from home:

Dear Parents,
To parents of a child with a serious life-threatening illness, the idea of using a hospice might imply a place of no hope, signifying defeat in everyone's attempts to cure the child. It did so to us when we first took our son home from hospital, still suffering from a tumour despite surgery and radiotherapy. We refused to give up hope that he might live and avoided Helen House, though several people had suggested that we could be helped there. Eventually, when we were tired and desperate and Martin was too ill to stay at home any longer, we came to look.

As soon as we saw the bright building, the cheerful faces, the beautiful furnishings and tempting toys, we knew that here was a place where Martin would be well cared for, our elder son would have fun and we would have a rest. It soon felt as if the staff shared our problems and it lightened our burden during the final weeks of Martin's life. If there is any hope for sick children it is here.

We do urge you to visit Helen House at the first opportunity – it doesn't have to be the last resort.

Yours sincerely, Susan and Derek Towe

Another parent, Barbara Hill, told me her reaction just after she had brought her son Chris here for the first time: 'They let you do as much or as little as you want. If you want to do it all, they'll let you do it all – but they're always there to lend a hand. Or if you want to go out anywhere, they'll let you go and they'll take over. . .but they don't sort of push; they don't take over as soon as you get here. You're free to do it all or nothing.'

From the staff's point of view Mother Frances said, 'We're not trying to do anything extraordinary or sophisticated, but just offering to stay alongside during the ups and downs of a child's illness – and afterwards – the period of bereavement is, if anything, even more lonely; and if our friendship is worth anything then it extends for as many months and years as the family wishes.' Helen House is at 37 Leopold Street, Oxford OX4 1QT. Tel. 0865 728251.

Helen House is very special; but it is no longer unique. Britain now has three other hospices for children, all dedicated to the same ideal and modelled closely on Mother Frances's experience.

At Wetherby in Yorkshire you will find Martin House with ten beds, including two for emergencies only. Several long years in the making, its opening was a triumph over all kinds of adversity by a determined group of local people. It took much advice from Helen House and has incorporated more space for parents – up to seven families can stay at any one time. But its reach is large – it can help in one way or another the families of 160 children. The full address is Martin House, Grove Road, Clifford, Wetherby, West Yorkshire LS23 6TS. Tel. 0937 845045.

Birmingham has Acorns, set up by the Children's Hospice Trust. The bulk of support they offer is in families' own homes, although they also provide a refuge for those needing a break. Many of their youngsters have metabolic and neurological degenerative disorders, and many more have progressive neuro-muscular disorders. In common with other children's hospice services, only a few have cancer. Their address is Acorns, 103 Oak Tree Lane, Selly Oak, Birmingham B29 6HZ. Tel. 021 414 1741.

The latest to open (in the summer of 1989) was in Cambridge. The Cambridge Children's Hospice Trust for East Anglia covers that region in the broadest sense, from Lincolnshire in the north down to London. Although most of its patients will be drawn from that area, it also accepts children from other parts of Britain. It stresses that it is not just for the terminally ill, but for all children and teenagers with 'a disorder that will not go away'. The maximum number it can cater for is twelve, with at least two of those beds free to take emergencies at short notice. The full address is Cambridge Children's Hospice Trust for East Anglia, Milton, Cambridge CB4 4AB. Tel. 0223 860306.

In 1989 there were also at least ten other children's hospice projects in the pipeline, ranging from some which were just starting to gather local support to others that were well advanced in their fund-raising. Not all will succeed! It needs more than a surge of local enthusiasm to carry such projects through from conception to operation. It requires long-term commitment, solid effort and clear planning to ensure that the project fits in with both local and national patterns of needs. And you will be surprised how many hospice projects end up providing and equipping the *building* without giving proper thought to the enormous cost of *running* it. The chapter on Setting up a Hospice will look at such pitfalls in greater detail. Suffice to say, a few aspects of development have so worried those who pioneered children's hospices in Britain that a national resource-information centre has been set up by the Institute of Child Health in Bristol whose Professor David Baum was one of the first paediatricians to back the concept of Helen House. Its symbol, appropriately enough, is an umbrella. Its name is ACT which stands for:

Action for the care of families whose
Children have life-threatening and
Terminal conditions.

Mother Frances summed up the thinking behind ACT:

We have long been aware of the need for a national centre where information could be collated on the existing services offering care and support to families whose children have life-threatening and terminal conditions. We have been concerned about wide gaps in liaison and co-ordination between those working in different ways in this field; this cannot be in the best interest of the children and families or, indeed, of those offering them care. Lack of communication can, of course, sometimes lead to initiatives being taken which are often extremely costly and might be considered inappropriate to the most pressing needs. We are therefore delighted that such an umbrella group, interlinking voluntary and statutory bodies involved in the care and support of these families, is being set up.

The particular emphasis of ACT will be on services which focus on home as the centre of care. So for advice and all forms of guidance in this delicate area, contact ACT, Institute of Child Health, Royal Hospital for Sick Children, St Michael's Hill, Bristol BS2 8BJ. Tel. 0272 221556 or 0272 215411, ext. 5558. Jill Pomerance and Jo Hearn have the answers at their fingertips!

Towards the end of 1989, as a progression of ACT, a national and advisory consultative board was set up to offer advice, guidance, help and support to anyone establishing and/or improving care for chronically sick children and their families. It was called ENACT or

Expertise available
Nationally to ensure
Action for the care of families whose
Children have life-threatening and
Terminal conditions.

The initial contact point is the same as for ACT.

There are, of course, a considerable number of parents who lose a child without having been anywhere near a hospice. Getting over that loss – coming to terms with it – can be a long process. Emotions run deep and can resurface again and again for years afterwards. Research has confirmed that members of families who have lost a child suffer a higher than normal rate of depression which requires medical treatment. There is also known to be a high chance of marital breakdown among bereaved parents. It is for such parents that the Alder Centre was opened in Liverpool in mid-1989. Based at the Royal Liverpool Children's Hospital, it offers a nationwide befriending and counselling service specifically for those who have lost a child and desperately need either considerable emotional help or simply a sympathetic and understanding ear. It recognizes that the effects of a child's death extend far beyond the immediate family and so it includes not just relatives but all those who have been involved in the child's care.

The Centre's full-time team works with volunteer parents who know and understand bereavement at first-hand. They are all there to comfort and, most important of all, to listen. People's needs vary. Some will be comforted by meeting others who have experienced a similar loss; others will benefit more from counselling on an individual basis; and there will be those who might prefer group counselling available at regular meetings of either informal 'drop-in' groups or more formal staff-led gatherings. A few months before the Alder Centre opened, a report on its planned work was broadcast on the 'Today' programme on BBC Radio 4. No one at the Centre could have anticipated the response. Their phone did not stop ringing for *four days*, with calls coming from as far afield as Glasgow and Plymouth, and people even enquiring whether they could come and stay at the Centre for a few days (it is *not* residential) – proof indeed of the need for such a service and justification of the eight years' work that has gone into setting it up. The Alder Centre has begun as a relatively small organization, with only two full-time staff – but can call on many volunteer parents who have been bereaved themselves and want to help. They also organize education and training for both professional and voluntary groups. The Centre is home for a Book of Remembrance – parents can have their child's name entered, along with a photograph or an inscription if they wish. The Book is kept permanently in a 'quiet room' where time can be spent peacefully. Future plans include a telephone 'help-line' for people with a sudden need to talk about their loss. The Alder Centre is at the Royal Liverpool Children's Hospital, Alder Hey, Eaton Road, Liverpool L12 2AP. Tel. 051 2284811.

Another organization that has enormous potential for national growth is Cancer and Leukaemia in Childhood (CLIC for short). At present it only covers south-west England but the unusual and highly cost-effective help it offers could make it a model for similar projects elsewhere. It is the brainchild of Dr Bob Woodward, a businessman who lost one child through cancer and another through Downs Syndrome. His fund-raising track record is impressive, based as it is on a strong local network of supporters; but it is what he does with the money that is so unusual. Instead of setting up a hospice, he looked at the *existing* services and asked what extra back-up was desirable to ease the difficulties of families with very sick children. Some of the answers are obvious – others are a fine example of lateral thinking.

CLIC funded the purchase of seven houses or flats near the specialist centres where children are treated and offers them *free of charge* to families who live long distances away from those centres. Thus CLIC removes the pressure on those families to make a tiring round trip in one day and solves their worries over the cost of accommodation – especially if a long course of regular treatment is involved. More than twenty families can be accommodated at any one time. CLIC has also established its own team of nine domiciliary care nurses, linked with clinics and ready to move into homes where help is needed. There are individual small personal grants to people with financial problems – perhaps one parent has to leave work to look after the child or there may be a need for new clothes because the cancer treatment is making the child gain or lose weight. Money might be given to cover the cost of renting videos or to pay for a fullscale family package holiday. And CLIC has even bought its own 'crisis-break flats' – two of them, close to the seaside, where families can enjoy free holidays. It puts money into research too. CLIC has a network of contacts throughout the south-west but its main office is at CLIC House, 11–12 Fremantle Square, Cotham, Bristol BS6 5TL. Tel. 0272 248844.

In Surrey there is Tadworth Court Children's Hospital, formerly an arm of Great Ormond Street and an independent charity since 1984 when it became the first operating hospital to leave the NHS. Its fifty-six-bed unit provides treatment for chronically sick, handicapped and terminally ill children. The relaxed, informal atmosphere creates a homely environment to which children are happy to return, and long-term and supportive relationships develop. Older children have single rooms to give privacy. There is an excellent hydrotherapy pool and a rehabilitation centre devoted to helping children whose brains have been injured through accident or illness; the highly qualified nursing and physiotherapy staff also have considerable experience in treating children with cystic fibrosis and chest problems. Ward-based out-patient clinics are held regularly and some children are seen under the 'shared-care' principle, being treated as out-patients in their own local hospitals and going to Tadworth Court only when they need in-patient treatment. Resident doctors are on call twenty-four hours a day, and consultant paediatricians visit regularly.

There is no separate hospice but Tadworth does offer short-term care for families who need a break, admitting children for a few days or a few weeks depending on circumstances, with beds always available for emergencies. A special holiday unit, open from May to September, enables handicapped children to have a holiday in pleasant surroundings, with outings and on-site activities arranged daily. Next door is an independent residential school for profoundly multi-handicapped children with severe learning difficulties. Write to The Nursing Manager, Tadworth Court Children's Hospital, Tadworth Court Trust, Tadworth, Surrey KT20 5RU. Tel. 0737 357171.

Also in Surrey, you will find the Rainbow Trust, a group of highly dedicated workers with a mass of experience in helping families in their own homes, living with them when necessary and providing an extra pair of hands when they face times of crisis with a child whose life is under threat. They help the family with domestic work, washing, ironing, cooking, shopping and baby-sitting. They also help with basic nursing skills, are trained in the art of listening and counselling, and will keep in touch for as long as they are needed. A respite/holiday centre is their latest project, offering support in a relaxed atmosphere to families with a terminally ill or chronically sick child. Their address is Rainbow Trust, Dove Cottage, 16 The Glade, Fetcham, Leatherhead, Surrey KT22 9TH.

Barnardos is funding a cystic fibrosis project which has strong links with hospitals in the Midlands. Its main purpose is to offer help in people's own homes; that help includes guidance on sources of funding, advice on equipment and liaison between services that might be needed. Much time is spent on counselling, particularly adolescents or parents whose new-born baby has just been diagnosed as having cystic fibrosis. In addition, they help to organize holidays and various excursions for children with the condition. You can write to them at The Cystic Fibrosis Project, Grosvenor Terrace, 90 Broad Street, Birmingham 15. Tel. 021 6333522.

They will also tell you about an identical Barnardo-funded project due to open in Nottingham as this book was being published. Both these operations have been greatly helped and encouraged by the Cystic Fibrosis Research Trust, founded in 1964 to research for a complete solution, and now with numerous groups of helpers from local to regional level. Untreated, a large proportion of CF children would die in early childhood, as they did thirty years ago; but early diagnosis and careful treatment, which need not interfere with a normal home and school life, is transforming the outlook, and more and more CF children are now emerging into early adulthood with relatively little lung damage. The risk of such damage, however, continues throughout life. The Trust does all it can to help CF sufferers in a wide variety of ways – from welfare advice to holiday caravans available in Britain for a nominal charge. For more details, contact the Cystic Fibrosis Research Trust, Alexandra House 5 Blyth Road, Bromley, Kent BR1 3RS. Tel. 01 464 7211/2.

For really special treats for all kinds of sick children, there is Dreams Come True, a charity set up by Margaret Hayles in 1982. Its aim is to bring some happiness into the lives of very sick and often terminally ill children, helping them to fight their illness by giving them something to live for – something to look forward to. So, for hundreds of children, dreams really have come true. Five-year-old Kelly, who had had a tumour removed from her stomach and lost one of her kidneys, met Orville; five-year-old Robert, who had a leg amputated because of cancer, met his idol, snooker champion Joe Johnson; and seven-year-old Michelle, who had lost both her eyes through cancer, was given the 'fluffy pussy cat' she had asked for. Everything from flights on Concorde or flying like Peter Pan to meeting pop stars or famous footballers is arranged, if it is at all possible. The address to write to is Dreams Come True Charity, 26 Gardner Street, Brighton BN1 1UP. Tel. 0273 670245.

Margaret Hayles herself has moved on to form another organization with a similar purpose, known as Sweet Dreams. She is based at Odintune Cottage, Odintune Place, Plumpton, Lewes, East Sussex. Tel. 0273 890243.

Increasingly, many of Britain's *hospitals* are offering home support in different ways for children with different conditions. It is impossible to list them all here, but it is worth checking locally to see what is available. To give you a sample of what is on offer – the Rupert Foundation funds a Symptom Care Team at Great Ormond Street Children's Hospital in London, consisting of a doctor and three nurses available to offer help in the home to cancer and leukaemia cases only. (Tel. 01 405 9200). Another, separate team at GOS visits children with brain tumours. Also in London, St Bartholomew's Hospital has a Community Support Paediatric Team (01 601 8888), and the Royal Marsden Cancer Hospital has three Community Nurses (01 642 6011). In Newcastle upon Tyne, the Royal Victoria Infirmary has two nurses available for cancer care, one more specializing in cystic fibrosis. (091 232 5131, ext 24788) And, by the end of 1989, Cancer Relief Macmillan Fund was financing its first three paediatric cancer nurses in Leicester, Manchester and Birmingham, with more on the way. These are just a few examples – but there are many other small groups, teams and individual scattered across the country who are too numerous to mention here – but who all help in different ways. Your local GP may well know about them – and you should in any case make a point of checking with ACT's office in Bristol (see p. 91).

New developments are coming along all the time. After the success of actor Paul Newman's holiday village in Connecticut, USA for children with life-threatening illnesses, a firm of London architects are currently examining the possibility of creating a similar project in Britain. And some existing centres in Britain are starting to set aside a few weeks each year to offer special holiday breaks. They are organized by Camp Quality UK, a charity set up in 1986 to provide free holidays for children with cancer and leukaemia. In response to many requests they are now extending their operations to embrace those with other life-threatening illnesses. Camp Quality have access to four camps in Devon, South Wales (two) and the Midlands (these are not, literally, camp sites – one is a manor house). The holidays are well run with plenty of support, including a fully qualified doctor and nurse, and contact is established with nearby hospitals in case of emergencies. The maximum number of children at each camp is thirty. For more information contact Mrs Earline Campbell, Camp Quality UK, 1 The Mews, Umberslade Hall, Tanworth-in-Arden, Warwickshire B94 5DF. Tel 05644 2098.

The 1980s have seen huge progress in the care of children with life-threatening illnesses in Britain. New ideas have been born, new buildings, new organizations have grown up; and, of course, there is always more to be done. But what strikes you most forcefully is the sheer dedication, commitment and professionalism of the wide range of people involved – professionals and volunteers – and the great depth of goodness that radiates from them, amazing and humbling both the casual passerby and parents who suddenly find they have a child who needs to walk their way.

9. POLITICS AND HOSPICES
The Party Policies

Hospices have never featured to any great extent in the election manifestos of Britain's main national political parties. Even though hospice work touches the lives of many people it has never become 'an issue' at elections. So it seemed reasonable and appropriate to ask the party leaders to go firmly on the record on this subject. All of them agreed to do so – the Prime Minister, Mrs Margaret Thatcher for the Conservative Party; the Leader of the Opposition, Mr Neil Kinnock, for the Labour Party; Mr Paddy Ashdown for the Democrats and Dr David Owen for the SDP. These are their unedited judgements on – and hopes for – the British hospice movement.

From the Prime Minister, Mrs Margaret Thatcher, Leader of the Conservative Party

The government is delighted that the publication of this *Handbook* coincides with Europe against Cancer Year. The key message across Europe is that cancer can be avoided and can be treated successfully, especially if it is detected at an early stage. Where a complete recovery is not possible, patients and their families need and deserve active help and support to live a full life, however long it lasts. Unfortunately, the fear of cancer still prevents some people from seeking the help they need at the earliest opportunity. The hospice movement, with its frank and open approach to death and dying, has made a significant contribution, not only to care, but also to breaking the silence on cancer and overcoming the fear.

The government, therefore, strongly supports the development of comprehensive and integrated services for people with a terminal illness. They and their families have many unique needs which can be met and which provide for a dignified and peaceful death. Over the past twenty years Britain has seen the development of terminal-care services involving the voluntary sector and the National Health Service. There is now an excellent network of hospices, home-care teams, day centres and hospital-based support teams. A tremendous amount of funding for these services comes from charitable giving and we value this contribution but, in addition, many now receive some government support. One third of the in-patient hospice units in the United Kingdom are in the National Health Service, as are most of the home-care teams and all the hospital-support teams. The government is indeed grateful to the many staff and volunteers who have given and continue to give so much of their time and love to care for patients with a terminal illness and members of their families. For such people, the hospice movement has developed a model of 'continuing care' which is used internationally.

The government's commitment to terminal care commenced in 1980 with the Report of a working party chaired by Professor Eric Wilkes on the organization of terminal-care services for people with cancer.[1] It continued with the major Conference on Care for the Dying held in London in 1985, at which HRH The Prince of Wales was the principal speaker.[2] The government's policy on terminal care is set out in a health circular, published by the Department of Health in 1987,[3] which asked the National Health Service to examine its current provision of services for all terminally ill patients, whatever their underlying disease or medical condition, and to plan to rectify any deficiencies where possible in collaboration with the voluntary sector. Health authorities are now working with some of the major charities both to expand and improve terminal-care services.

From Mr Neil Kinnock, Leader of the Labour Party

As I know from the experience of my own family, the hospice movement is a practical and merciful response to human need.

Hospices represent the highest ideals of our community as they seek to offer the best care to all who need it, irrespective of income or status. They have taken the medical and the moral offensive against death as a painful, lonely and fearful end to life.

There are so many ways of measuring the achievements of

1. 'Terminal Care' - the Report of a Working Group of the Standing Medical Advisory Committee's Standing Sub-Committee on Cancer, published by the Department of Health, London, 1980.
2. 'Conference on Care for the Dying' proceedings, published by HMSO in 1986.
3. 'Terminal Care' health circular HC(87)4, issued by the Department of Health, London, 1987.

hospices in individual terms. They 'do it unto the least of these' and countless numbers of people have had, and will have, cause to be grateful to them. But amongst their greatest accomplishments is the fact that, from the slums of Soweto to the wealthy suburbs of New York, the techniques of the gentle and compassionate medicine first developed in the hospice movement in Britain now cross the borders of geography, language and culture. That model, inspired by Cicely Saunders twenty-one years ago, has offered a new dimension in medicine and care.

Within the UK the hospice movement has grown rapidly in the past twenty-one years. There are now 133 voluntary hospices; 40,000 patients are treated each year. The statistics tell a small part of the real story of what is achieved every day throughout the country. There are no operating theatres and no high technology, just highly skilled, highly trained nursing care, counselling and support for the dying and, for the loved ones they leave behind, help to cope with the terrible loss.

Of course, the hospice movement does not limit itself to residential care. It reaches out into homes. Where day care is appropriate for the mortally ill, the hospice helps to support the family. But where it is not possible, the hospice creates an atmosphere that is as much like home as possible. There is no end to willing care whether it means, as it has done in one hospice in the East End of London, lending out the hospice canary to cheer up house-bound patients, finding a job for family relatives or arranging visits to patients by relatives from prison.

The work doesn't stop there. The techniques and treatments pioneered by the hospice movement are welcomed and adopted throughout many NHS hospitals as nurses, doctors and other staff at all levels make efforts to ensure that their hospitals are as hospitable, as comfortable and comforting as possible for those in the greatest distress.

My ambitions for health care in this country include arrangements for NHS hospitals to have more opportunity to apply more of the techniques of hospice care for their patients. It can be done and, as the numbers of elderly people in our population increase, it must be done. Healers and helpers of all kinds in the health professions fear, however, that such an advance will either be very difficult or impossible within a 'reformed' NHS in which hospitals are encouraged financially to opt out of community care and to offer the cheapest treatment for the most rapid turnover.

In such a programme – it would be much less of a service – the vital trust and confidence between doctor and patient would be under great strain and the chronically sick and the elderly would soon find themselves at the back of the queue. Clearly, nothing would be further from the ideals of the NHS or the hospice movement. And to keep those ideals intact in practice, as well as in purpose, it is important that our provision for the care of illness in our country does not become subject to the pressures of 'opting out' and all that it means.

Hospices, with the emphasis they put on interdisciplinary skills, on care for the whole person and care for the individual and the family, have shown us the direction in which modern medicine and terminal care must go. But it must be a partnership of resources and skill. Just as I want to see every member of the health team have the time, the scope and the training to help those who are terminally ill and their families through this last human barrier with comfort and dignity, so I want to see the hospice movement developing in confidence, knowing that it has the financial security to maximize what it can offer best. Dr Anne Gilmore, Director of the Prince and Princess of Wales Hospice in Glasgow, has said that stress comes not from a career helping people who are dying but from 'the limitations imposed on the type of care that can be given'. Every NHS nurse and doctor knows that only too well. Every patient and potential patient has a direct interest in seeing that such limitations are removed. None of us, when faced with pain or death – particularly when they threaten our loved ones – will want less than the best for them. And we will want that standard without 'limitation'.

The hospice movement values its independence, I applaud that. It liberates the humanity and the skill of the whole community. And that independence can be strengthened if more financial support is available from health authorities which need and use hospices and would like to be able to extend that relationship. Within a modernized National Health Service I would want to see sufficient resources liberated to hospice care on a systematic basis, where hospices want that support. In addition, it is essential that a complete commitment is made to ensuring that the skilled nursing care within hospices is treated four-square with NHS nursing staff – and fully rewarded, regraded and funded.

If those obvious and necessary steps are taken, the NHS and the hospice movement can move forward in proper partnership towards health care which offers the highest standards of individual care and dignity throughout the *whole* of life. In that way, while none of us can defeat death, we can at least ensure that so much of the suffering that comes with it can be eased by the people and the spirit which made and now maintains the hospices.

From Mr Paddy Ashdown, Leader of the Social & Liberal Democrats

The basis of our policy and recommendations should be that death, and the preparation for it, are as essential a part of the life process as birth, and should be treated with equal care and respect in the National Health Service.

This quote, taken from a previous Liberal document, still stands as our most fundamental statement of principle on the care of the dying. We have no 'ideal' location for death, whether at home, in hospital, a nursing home or hospice, but it is our belief that the patient must be informed and given every possible option. The resulting choice must be given the utmost respect by the system.

And while we make no decision for the individual, we recognize that the hospice movement is at the forefront of sensitive, informed care and, as such, should be established as a model for technique and as a resource and teaching centre for all carers of the dying.

Realistically, however, the average citizen is more likely to begin and finish this journey in the hospital and never experience hospice care. Thus, to discuss hospice care without its counterparts would be misleading and, therefore, we place it in its context as a part of our policy on the care of the dying.

Home Care

The first, and often most problematical, obstacle for those who take on the responsibility of caring for the dying at home is the cost which can accompany this task. We believe that the benefit system should be altered so families or primary carers of the terminally ill can have immediate access to funds through the introduction of a carer's benefit. A sixth-month waiting period is absurd when dealing with a seriously ill person who must have certain items to stay at home. Counselling and education should be also available to the family and friends of the patient, and include preparation for the death, discussion on issues which may occur such as sudden death, life support, funeral arrangements and organ donation. Another problem for home carers is the lack of respite and day care. We believe these should be available, ranging from day or night volunteers to temporary in-patient care.

Hospital and Nursing-home Care
The problem of traditional hospital care has been that, while staff are highly trained to keep people alive, they are not especially skilled in helping them deal with death. This fundamental revision of attitude is difficult and, without training, can leave emotional scars on both patient and staff; this is why the education and availability of counselling for professionals is a crucial area for improvement. All carers of the dying should be educated in bereavement counselling, religious and cultural differences, medical treatments and their side effects, palliative *vs.* curative care, and both medical and emotional alternatives to traditional care. The introduction of the Project 2000 reforms of nursing education gives us an excellent opportunity to add these elements to traditional nurse training.

Education in many of these same areas is also equally important to the patient. One way to deal with this situation is to encourage dialogues between patients and staff about issues such as life-support efforts, organ donation and the death of others known to the patient. Outside counselling should be available for staff and patient where requested. There have been many discussions on the use of designated wards for dying patients and, while we believe this should be presented to the patient as an option, we feel that there may be a danger of them becoming a dumping ground for patients.

Also, many people want to stay within the wards and not feel as if they have been sent off to die. These wishes must be respected. Hospitals should also be able to draw on spiritual guides of all religious backgrounds. Finally, hospitals should co-ordinate outside care with the advice of a hospice centre of care to give the patient the full range of options. Where hospice resource information is not available funds should be allocated for this purpose.

Nursing-home staff, specifically, should have more access to training in the care of the dying and participate in hospice training. Again, hospices should be used as resources to assist in the co-ordination of care for patients and to place them in situations appropriate to their needs.

Hospice Care

Our initial statements of principle have many applications for the general care of terminally ill patients but their application to the hospice movement is most salient. Dame Cicely Saunders brought a new age of openness and honesty to death and the dying; but, as the country that is renowned for being the home of this movement, we have sadly not lived up to its promise.

Hospices in this country are still predominantly in the private sector. They are only now, through the public attention given to AIDS hospices, growing out of their image of being exclusively for cancer patients. But the education of professionals still does not reflect the necessary sensitivity and, above all, the system is still not designed with the dignity and self-respect of the terminal patient at its heart.

As a party, we believe that hospices should become the hub of treatment for the dying and given the funding necessary to take an active role in planning, co-ordinating, training and implementing this care. Our specific proposals include:

- funding for hospice care, especially hospices that also offer home, respite, day and follow-up care;
- investigation of the prospects of opening hospices for those with other diseases who would benefit from the individual attention of the hospice environment, and the prospect for general hospices investigated;
- hospices to be used as community resource/teaching facility/counselling centres for those involved in the treatment of the dying, whether at home, in hospital or other facility.

Conclusion

Our society seems to be rediscovering that death is as much a part of the pattern of life as birth and the living of it. But that process of rediscovery is still new and sometimes frightening to a society that spends millions of pounds every year to distance itself from the pain and natural processes associated with these first two acts. There are many other proposals which could be put forward, but essentially our party believes that the final question for each proposal must always be: will this promote information, choice and dignity for the dying?

Albert Goldsworthy at Nightingale Macmillan
Continuing Care unit at Derby.

Sidney Haines at Sir Michael Sobell House, Oxford.

Molly Harris (glioma) exercising with a zimmer and two physiotherapists.

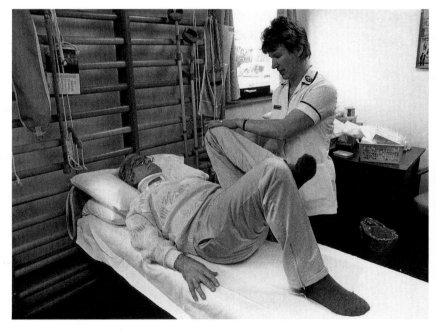

Gordon (Bill) Fountain (M.N.D.) with physiotherapist, Barbara.

From Dr David Owen, Leader of the SDP

The growth of hospices, Macmillan teams and allied services for the dying has been a remarkable achievement. The pioneers from Mary Aikenhead and Douglas Macmillan to Cicely Saunders and their followers have brought about a revolution in the way we can care for those approaching the end of life. This revolution is all the more remarkable because it encompasses not just medicine and nursing, but the whole attitude to death and the way patients should be cared for. Put simply, hospices have taught us that patients are always to be cherished, and most of all during their dying days.

The hospice revolution has been led by the voluntary and charity sectors. Hospice development has frequently been in the face of professional scepticism, and sometimes even in the face of downright professional opposition. It has won through, however, because of the tenacity of the pioneers, and because of enormous public support and goodwill. Above all, the hospice story demonstrates what a vital role the voluntary and charity sectors can play in providing new and better health and social services.

But whereas the voluntary and charity sectors can pioneer and innovate, and provide a lead, they cannot be expected to take on the whole task of caring for dying patients. That would be to turn the whole ethos of the National Health Service on its head. The NHS must welcome co-operation with the voluntary sector. The NHS must not be allowed to exploit the voluntary sector.

The policy of the SDP is based upon one fundamental principle. It is that all patients dying with acute and chronic illness have the right to receive the best possible medical, nursing and social care.

SDP policy is therefore to ensure that this care is available whether patients are cared for in a hospice, in an ordinary hospital, or in their own homes. This policy has four elements:

1. That terminal care must be recognized as a core service for health authorities in the same way as maternity care. The NHS ideal of providing care from 'the cradle to the grave' must become a reality.
2. There should be basic standards for the medical and nursing care of the dying to guide both the NHS and the voluntary sector. Such standards cannot be measured in cash terms. They must indicate desired standards and not minimum ones.
3. Health authorities must make available adequate financial

support for voluntary hospices in their areas which provide care of a proper standard for NHS patients.

4. The care of the dying patient should become an established part of the curriculum for medical and nursing students and a part of continued training for both hospital and community doctors and nurses.

10. SETTING UP A HOSPICE
The Problems and Pitfalls

To be touched by the hospice movement is to be inspired by it too. It can encourage a degree of voluntary help and support which is amongst the highest levels of giving in a community. But if a community does not have a hospice, then the desire to help often becomes a wish to create one. It is not a task that should be undertaken lightly.

Since Dame Cicely's success with St Christopher's Hospice, hundreds of highly motivated and caring people have tried to follow her example. Most have succeeded – but not without much worry, heartache, frustration and moments when it seemed failure was staring them in the face. Expert guidance was seldom available to the degree they would have liked – not only because the learning curve for such a relatively young movement was high, but also because each hospice has to be closely geared to the often unique requirements of the community it serves. Local jealousies and politics occasionally blurred the purpose and delayed or denied completion of the work. Some newcomers, acting from the very best of motives, were so fired up with enthusiasm and vision that they blinded themselves to the financial and operational practicalities involved. They refused to take advice from people with experience – and if you do not know how to listen, you fail.

Only now, towards the end of the 1980s, has it been possible to distill the wealth of experience gained across two decades of modern hospice-creation and lay down some ground rules to guide those who seek to follow. In doing so I have drawn heavily on some excellent research by the Department of Community Medicine at Sheffield University Medical School. In a series of surveys, they examined the experiences of every in-patient unit and day hospice in the country (both NHS and voluntary) throughout 1988, seeking the opinions of medical directors, matrons, administrators, social workers and volunteers. They emphasized that they were not 'setting out a series of laws or injunctions, but a set of propositions which anyone setting up or running a Hospice needs to consider, whether or not such

propositions are finally incorporated into practice'. What follows
is a summary of their conclusions.

Governing Boards and Committees

All hospices outside the NHS, i.e., most of them, are run as
charities; they have to be registered with the Charity Commission
(or its equivalent in Scotland and Northern Ireland). Trustees
should make sure they are fully aware of the legal responsibilities
and duties that are part and parcel of the job. Membership should
not be seen as 'a feather in one's cap', but as a deep and serious
commitment to keep fully in touch with the complete range of
hospice activities.

Members of the governing board, who are responsible for
establishing policy and planning for future development, should
meet regularly and publish an annual report and accounts. A copy
of the accounts should be filed with the central register of the
Charity Commissioners. The governing board is responsible for
high standards of patient care which can only be achieved by
appointing experienced staff of a high calibre to manage the
hospice on a day-to-day basis; so the selection panel should
include members with direct experience in the relevant fields.

Some tasks such as fund-raising or educating people about
hospice work could be delegated to special committees –
although fund-raisers should not dictate, nor be involved in, the
actual management of the hospice; they raise money for purposes
which are decided by the hospice management team and the
governors, though it is, of course, possible for a fund-raiser also
to be a member of the governing board.

The responsibilities of those who run the hospice unit on a day-
to-day basis should be clearly defined; they should report
regularly to the board and, if that board is particularly large, i.e.,
fifteen or more, its members should avoid putting undue direction
or pressure on the management team – that has been known to
cause enormous difficulties which impede the smooth running of
the hospice. Governors and committee members should consider
holding office for only a limited period of time, and with a stated
age limit, as the hospice movement is growing and developing and
there must be room for new faces and new ideas. It is best if such
limits are embodied in the 'governing instrument' of the hospice.

Early Planning

It is absolutely vital that those planning any form of hospice care consult their health authorities as early as possible. For a start, Regional Health Authorities have to submit plans for terminal care in their districts to the Department of Health; the big danger, however, is that hospice units springing up in a totally unco-ordinated way may find it difficult to attract the resources and support they need for survival in the long-term – especially if the catchment area for a particular hospice covers more than one authority area.

It is perfectly true that some hospices have preferred to 'go it alone' to overcome what they see as unnecessary bureaucracy or, in some cases, because their local health authority refused to give any help at all. But the end to those kind of difficulties may be in sight, especially since the government asked the health authorities (in no uncertain terms) to spell out precisely what each of them was doing to help terminal care. In any case, now is the time to kiss and make up with your local health authority as you may need them when some of the early fund-raising enthusiasm has waned!

Look very carefully at local needs and how they match up with existing resources provided by both the NHS and the voluntary sector. It may be more appropriate at first to establish a home-care or day-hospice facility, with the provision of back-up beds through co-operation with local hospital consultants. An in-patient unit can then be built later when experience has shown precisely what is required.

Once the hospice service is in operation, it is important to work as closely as possible with the NHS. Hospice skills should be offered without appearing élitist or critical of hospital or community care – one of the big unintended problems of the movement's early days. The hospice pattern of care may increasingly be seen as pointing the way to the future, but there are still quite a few converts to be made along the way – especially amongst those who have been doing it differently for some time and see no need to change.

Senior personnel should be aware of how important it is to develop good relations with the local community – they can be a powerful source of funding and volunteer help. (More on this in the chapter on fund-raising.)

The Management

Every hospice should have a clearly defined management structure which is obvious to both staff and public. Although in some smaller institutions there may be some overlapping of roles at times, it is vital that each staff member should have a clear, unambiguous outline of his or her responsibilities – and that this should be written into the contract of employment. Bureaucratic professionalism should be avoided! As one seasoned senior hospice worker put it, 'Avoid administering the soul out of a hospice.'

A hospice has only one objective – the welfare of the patient and his family. The management should encourage regular assessment of the care and services provided – and of its own structure, policies and practices. Stagnation and false complacency are the prime enemies. Regular staff appraisal might be carried out by the hospice's multi-disciplinary team. Occasionally, outsiders could be called in to evaluate and advise on particular aspects.

The Administrator

Some very small independent units may be administered and managed by the medical director and the matron; but above a certain size – and this may be as small as six beds – an administrator should be appointed as an essential hospice officer. He or she should have some experience of this type of role e.g., in hospital administration, and should be familiar with company and charity law and general employment legislation. The panel appointing this administrator should include a member experienced in the appointment of senior staff to organizations. Public relations are important – whoever is chosen will have to show versatility and good humour within the hospice, and be a good salesman of the hospice ideal to those who still need convincing in the surrounding community.

The Hospice Team

Terminal care means team care – ranging from a medical director, nurses and therapists to social workers, volunteers, clergymen and some whose advice is available on request. It is vital that the team develops a good working relationship with the patient's GP, other members of the primary health care team and hospital consultants. To ensure clinical care is always available, the hospice must employ, or have the services of, more than one particular doctor.

A Medical Director

The medical director ensures that the full range of modern hospice care is provided. He or she will, in most if not all cases, be top of the internal management tree and must have clear leadership qualities, be fully trained and experienced in the fields of palliative and terminal care and show a spirit of enquiry into new knowledge. The post may be full-time or part-time, depending on the size of the unit.

Other Medically Qualified Staff

These are needed to cover for the medical director e.g., GPs with a special interest in terminal care or junior doctors training for general practice or oncology. Permanent appointments have the advantage of guaranteeing continuity of style and approach in care and treatment.

Nursing Staff

The *matron* (senior nursing office) is a key figure in any hospice unit. She is responsible for providing all nursing care and will need good managerial skills as well as a particular interest in the care of the dying. It is a full-time post with cover provided for absence.

Trained nurses, preferably with some post-registration experience, should form the majority of professional hospice staff. Their ratio to patients will be greater than one-to-one overall. They can be full-time or part-time (many nurses who left the profession to bring up families are often happy to return if they can be offered a less stressful, shorter working week). Experience in other nursing areas such as community nursing, oncology, geriatric, orthopaedic and mentally handicapped is, of course, an enormous help. Auxiliary nurses, who provide the 'mothering' skills usually given by a family member at home, are invaluable for terminal care and they usually include older, married women, as well as young people taking their first steps into nursing.

Many nurses (up to 50 per cent in some hospices) come for short periods from the NHS to learn hospice skills, with every intention of returning either to community or hospice care taking this knowledge with them.

Advice on Tap

Volunteers

They are of huge benefit to a hospice and have to be carefully selected and properly deployed, supervised and supported. A paid Volunteers' Organizer should be appointed to co-ordinate the wide range of activities in which they play a part e.g., drivers, hairdressers, occupational therapy assistants. Hours should be flexible. As well as their practical contribution, volunteers help break down the barriers and fears that often surround patients. It is vital to have volunteers involved with permanent staff right from day one. Selection should be on the basis of a personal interview and references – the interview being the more important as the first test is of the person rather than their skills. They should have support at home and sufficient time and energy to spare for voluntary work. Recruitment is improved by good public relations between the hospice and the community. Widespread advertising is to be avoided. Training courses are essential – as are firm guidelines (and perhaps signed undertakings) on confidentiality. It can be a full-time or part-time job.

Social Worker

In many units, the nursing staff give 'family support' over and above their normal work; many (if not most) bereavement counsellors are specially trained volunteers; and in some cases social workers have not been regarded as indispensable members of the care team. But it is now recognized that social workers have much to offer and that, ideally, there should be one social worker whose main commitment is to the hospice. There are now some 120 members of the Association of Hospice Social Workers who meet regularly the Hospice Information Service at St Christopher's (01 778 9252) will have the up-to-date contact point.

The Clergy

Spiritual care is an integral part of the modern hospice movement. There are many difficult questions to face. So local clergymen will be familiar faces, administering to patients' religious needs – and often supporting staff. But they should not be expected to give all the spiritual and emotional support in a unit; clear definition of roles is vital. Non-believers also need comfort and support and though many may prefer to talk to other members of staff there are occasions when a chaplain is formally involved. Coercion to take part in services, or attempts to convert a patient or relative, must be resisted by senior members of the hospice team. Hospices have firm rules about this.

The Association of Hospice Chaplains can be contacted via the Rev. Colin Kassell, St Catherine's Hospice, Malthouse Road, Crawley, Sussex RH10 6BH. Tel. 0293 547333.

Other Therapists

Physiotherapy and occupational therapy can make valuable contributions to the rehabilitation of patients. The maintenance of maximum mobility of a patient is particularly appreciated, as are other improvements to the activities of daily living and the quality of life. Occupational therapy offers a range of diversions and skill-development which give pleasure and comfort to patients confined to bed or attending a day hospice; it also enables them to keep their faculties alert.

A relatively new development has been the increased emphasis on the arts and music in hospices – 'the healing role of the arts', as some describe it. In hospices it is by no means as widespread as some would like but, where it has been tried, its impact has been substantial. It takes many forms. Sharing favourite melodies and old-time songs helps reminiscence and reflection. So do taped books. Encouraging patients to write poetry has been a great success, due to the pioneering efforts of Jane Eisenhauer at St Joseph's Hospice in Hackney. Other projects include artists working with graphic arts, with fabrics and with flower arranging. Entertainment can be arranged through individual contact and through organizations like the Council for Music in Hospitals.[1] In America, the public health code of the state of Connecticut says, 'the Hospice shall provide extensive opportunities for experiences in arts to patient and family. . .the director of arts shall be considered a fully fledged member of the health care team'.

In Britain, a consultant physician, David Frampton, now working at Chelmsford Hospice, eased the path for pioneering

---

1. The Council for Music in Hospitals can be contacted at 340 Lower Road, Little Bookham, Surrey KT23 4EF. Tel. 0372 58264.

artists. And in the summer of 1989, Britain's first Director of Hospice Arts was appointed – funded mainly by the Forbes Trust and Help the Hospices, with some extra help from the Gulbenkian Foundation.[1] David Frampton, in an early project, wrote about students at the Guildhall School of Music visiting a hospice to play to the patients:

Not only does this give a boost to the patient, but our previous experience has shown the considerable impact on the students of such contact with some of the painful realities of life when they attempt to relate their musical skills to them.

Similar developments include 'Invitation to the Ballet'[2] – an award winning project by the Royal Ballet to take dancers into hospices and hospitals. A few home-care teams have volunteer artists who visit patients in their own homes. Help the Hospices is now involved in providing training for artists – helping them to find the best way to adjust their particular art forms and techniques to the patient's failing strength and limited concentration.

And if patients can reach out to these new and encouraging areas of hospice activity, they can reach back into the past as well. Dr Peter Kaye, at Cynthia Spencer House in Northampton, has made a detailed study showing how important it is to help patients reminisce. He has clearly demonstrated how uplifting it is for patients to talk to someone who probes and triggers the major memories of their lives. The address is Cynthia Spencer House, Mansfield Hospital, Northampton NN3 1AD. Tel. 0604 491121.

The Hospice Building

The size of the in-patient unit should be in keeping with the needs of the community. Consideration should be given to the catchment area covered by the hospice and to the availability of other similar facilities provided in the locality by charities or the NHS. A survey by Frank Hill and Christine Oliver in mid-1988 found that the lowest costs per bed per week were in units with between twenty and twenty-nine beds; and the highest costs in units with

1. Hospice Arts is based at the Forbes Trust, 9 Artillery Lane, London EC1 7LP.
2. 'Invitation to the Ballet' is via the Education Department, Royal Opera House, Covent Garden, London WC2.

between five and nine beds. So the small home-like hospices that appear most popular are less economically efficient. Looking at it from a purely economic point of view, overall cost effectiveness appears to be at its best in units containing more than thirty-five beds although many hospices would not require so many. Of course, the effect of volunteer labour can significantly reduce the cost of in-patient care, but against this must be weighed the cost of fund-raising which, as hospices begin to compete for funds, is definitely on the increase.

The in-patient unit must allow access and movement of beds and wheelchairs to all patient areas. Easy access from the street is also required. The interior of the building should have plenty of light and provide a pleasant external view. Gardens, fountains, aviaries and fishponds are attractive amenities, as are flower beds laid at wheelchair height for patients to take part in the care of plants.

Maximum privacy for patients should be the aim and as many single rooms as possible should be provided. Space for an extra bed in the room and privacy for a relative to stay overnight is welcomed. Other accommodation for relatives, sited near to that of the patient is desirable. Where single rooms are not available, four beds in a ward have proved satisfactory, each patient being in an area of his or her own. To increase privacy, it is an advantage if beds are not placed directly opposite each other.

Provision should be made for the patient's bedside to be equipped for radio, television, audio tapes and a mobile telephone. An audio tape library is an asset. Facilities for patients to do personal laundry and prepare snacks are appreciated (though Food Hygiene Regulations have to be complied with).

A room, or at least a space, should be set aside as a quiet room, a chapel, or for a variety of religious purposes. Participation in a religious service should be entirely voluntary and the patient's views must be respected by staff and other patients. It is also important to provide facilities for teaching and training sessions for local doctors, nurses, chaplains, and all those involved.

Some toilets, baths and showers should be suitable for use by the disabled and so designed that they can be used independently of a nurse. A separate toilet and washroom for nurses and visitors is recommended.

The need for office and storage space should not be under-estimated. Separate offices should be provided for heads of departments, the home-care team (present or planned) and administration staff.

Choosing the right site and right design for the building is extremely important. Of course, if an old building is being converted, options are limited; but if a totally new building is planned, it is worth looking at a new computer-aided design system introduced by Cancer Relief Macmillan Fund to cut dramatically both the time and costs involved. Called 'Macmillan Green': it encapsulates all the recent advances in this field of care which have done so much to improve patients' quality of life. It is extremely cost effective and so flexible in design that it can easily be adapted to different locations and site requirements.

The central feature of the new unit is the 'Green': located in the middle of the building, and occupying the largest single space, this is a day-care area similar in function to a village green. It offers extensive facilities for social activities and occupational therapy and also gives direct access to all other accommodation, as well as terraces and gardens. It is the hub of the patient-care community and emphasizes the very central role of day and home care in this service. The Green is both an architectural device and a key factor in the flexibility of the building design. It acts as a 'junction box' around which one can 'plug-in', lego-like, a range of pre-designed accommodation blocks including day-care support unit, in-patient ward, teaching unit, a coffee bar, occupational therapy and TV areas, hairdressing/beauty salon, etc. There is no blueprint for arranging these modules which can be positioned entirely to suit users' needs and to meet any particular site requirements. The carefully planned modules are stored on a computer database so architects are able to respond quickly to individual projects at a very early stage in the planning process. Cancer Relief are at pains to point out that the use of this computer technology does *not* mean system building. The great flexibility of the design concept ensures that each Macmillan Green will look different and have its own unique atmosphere.

Although the considerable advances in the care of cancer patients are now recognized by the NHS, they have yet to be implemented systematically. Cancer Relief believes that Macmillan Green offers one way by which health authorities and voluntary groups can draw up a strategy to provide full care and support for the maximum number of patients and their relatives. Cancer Relief are encouraging them to site these units near oncology and radiotherapy departments in hospitals to enable close collaboration between these two fields of care. Day hospices based on the concept are under construction in Newbury and Wokingham; another is planned at Dellwood, near Reading (with its own in-patient unit); and some existing hospices are using the modules to develop expansion plans. Full details from Cancer Relief Macmillan Fund, Anchor House, 15–19 Britten Street, London SW3 3TY. Tel. 01 351 7811.

An invaluable booklet, called *So Birchester Needs a Hospice* . . .(£5 inc. p & p), is available from the Department of Community Medicine, Sheffield University Medical School, Beech Hill Road, Sheffield S10 2RX. Tel. 0742 766222. It includes invaluable check-lists of questions would-be hospice creators should ask themselves at every stage of the process.

A copy of the full report/surveys on which the booklet is based costs £10, as does a separate 1985 report from the same department – 'Home Care Services for the Terminally Ill: a Report for the Nuffield Foundation' by A.W.M. Ward.

Through all the traumas, difficulties, clashes of egos and local politics involved in setting up a hospice, please don't forget Dame Cicely Saunders's advice: a hospice only works if it *listens*!

11. FUND-RAISING FOR YOUR LOCAL HOSPICE

More than half all in-patient hospices are independent free-standing units, usually charities in their own right. The latest official survey – at the end of December 1987 – found that seventy-two of the (then) 122 hospices received just 27 per cent of their overall funding from the NHS. For the eleven Marie Curie hospices the figure was 8 per cent; for the six Sue Ryder hospices it was 10 per cent; and for the thirteen Macmillan, thirteen NHS units and seven Macmillan mini-units the government provided the full 100 per cent. So the overall figure that shows the NHS providing just over one third of all hospice funding conceals huge disparities across the country. It does not take account of the 250 or so home-care teams which are highly cost-effective and usually end up with considerable local health authority support. But, on the other hand, it does not allow for widely differing attitudes found from one health authority to another. Some make a major effort to help – others go out of their way not to.

It has been suggested that the more recalcitrant ones deliberately put the hospice at, or near, the bottom of their list of financial priorities because it is the most powerful emotional argument when they are trying to persuade the government to raise their budgets. And besides, they argue, when the hospices appear to be doing so well raising cash from charitable sources, why give them money that could be spent on something else? The government tried to concentrate their minds rather more firmly on the subject in 1988 by sending out a letter asking every single health authority to spell out what provision they were making for terminal care – indeed, requiring them to draw up a specific programme for doing so. The response from the traditional heel-draggers was generally not as fast or as detailed as had been hoped.

In the survey conducted for this *Handbook* in February 1989 I asked hospices what they hoped for in the way of extra funding – compared to six months earlier. Not all answered that question. Of the 158 that did, twenty-six thought their funding would be higher, thirteen reckoned it would be lower and 119 thought it would be exactly the same. St Andrew's Hospice in Grimsby added the following rider: 'Even with the impetus of the DHSS to require authorities to respond, such are the delaying tactics that our authority has no plans to outline any programme until the end of 1989 – for its next planning cycle.' Hospice Care for Burnley and Pendle said their district health authority offered plenty of encouragement but no prospect of any *financial* help. And the Macmillan Home Care service at Carmarthen reports that their health authority 'has no intentions of improving the service in the near future'.

St Catherine's Hospice in Preston outlines an even more fundamental problem:

We receive no assistance from the Department of Social Services for terminal care. A patient entitled to receive benefit when in a fee-paying (and profit-making) nursing home can receive up to £235 a week. Because Hospices do not, on principle, charge patients, the DSS will sometimes decline to pay. Their argument is that, since the patient is not out of pocket, they have no obligation.

That, it must be said, is not a universal reaction – the hospice charities say there are many local DSS offices that understand the requirements of patients in hospices and provide the residential allowance for terminally ill patients who satisfy the criteria.

There is another Catch–22 which can make it difficult, if not impossible, for a terminally ill patient in a hospice to claim an attendance allowance for some six months – by which time it may well be too late. There are also difficulties for patients in the sheer complexity of the forms which have to be filled in and the rules for payment. The DSS, however, are aware of the unsuitability of certain benefits regulations and are looking for ways to adapt the system to the specific needs of hospice patients.

The nurses' pay award and regrading in 1988 piled on another layer of financial pressure, adding up to 20 per cent to hospices' annual running costs.

So, overall, hospices have to look to their own resources – their own fund-raising operations – for some 60 per cent of their income. Obviously, those that have to find the full 100 per cent live the most precarious existence, subject to the cyclical vagaries and increasing competition of the charity market-place. There is no doubt that, in many of those hospices, staff and volunteers spend a disproportionate amount of time fund-raising outside the building at the expense of hope-raising within it. How much more time could they devote to the patient if just some of that financial burden was lifted? I say 'just some' because there is no doubt that the social activity engendered by fund-raising creates a strong bond between community and hospice. People feel they are giving to a cause that is both important and close to them. That gives them a sense of pride and pleasure. It would be wrong to remove that – but people's pockets don't always run deep enough. And now hospices are encountering new competition from health authorities starting to employ their own fund-raisers to try to tap into some of the very sources of income that the hospices depend upon. Admittedly, it is a measure of the tremendous support that hospices enjoy around the country that, in modern times, not one of them has ever closed down through lack of money. But some continue to run unnecessarily and alarmingly close to the precipice.

Where, then, does their charitable funding come from? The survey for this *Hospice Handbook* showed that some 28 per cent came from individual donations – mainly people who had experienced a hospice as either patients, relatives or friends, and were so grateful and impressed they wanted to help. The national charities involved in hospices and cancer care contribute 13 per cent. Bequests provide 11 per cent. Eight per cent came from charitable trusts and 5 per cent from the profits of the hospices' own charity shops. (There is the potential for much greater development here. Princess Alice Hospice in Esher now has a network of twelve such shops, run highly effectively by no fewer than 600 volunteers – all taking their turn behind the counter – and expecting a turnover of half a million pounds in 1989.) A further 5 per cent came from the business community; and – reflecting the effort of the many dedicated volunteers – a whopping 17 per cent came from other fund-raising activities such as raffles, jumble sales, etc. Ideas that may help those activities grow even more are outlined towards the end of this chapter.

There are few causes as consistently powerful as hospices for bringing out the very best in people – few charities that find themselves so closely linked to the communities they serve. Many hospices have grown from local initiatives. In a world where no one can say with any certainty they will not need a hospice tomorrow, today's givers know they could be tomorrow's patients. That may well be a powerful factor in fund-raising.

One of the first people to demonstrate how to tap widely into that potential was the Rev. Tom Scott of Strathcarron Hospice near the Scottish town of Stirling. Years before the government introduced tax relief on payroll giving, Tom Scott canvassed every business and factory, within thirty miles of his Hospice, and asked each management to ask every member of its workforce if he or she would be prepared to donate either 5 or 10p a week to Strathcarron – deducted through the company payroll and paid directly with one single cheque each month. The idea took off. People who might draw back if you stopped them in the street and asked for a £5 donation thought nothing of giving £5 a year in the shape of 10p a week. As one secretary put it, 'You don't notice that it's gone.' An electrician remembered that 'My granny died up there – sure I'll help.' And a computer operator said she was giving 'because you never know when you might be there yourself'. Whatever the motives, Tom Scott found himself pulling in over £30,000 a year. That was in the early eighties – by 1989 he was heading towards the £100,000 mark; and the tax relief now available on payroll giving (available on up to £480 a year since the budget of March 1989) offers hospices considerable opportunity to, literally, cash in on their close links with the community. The best approach is to lobby the employers – either individually or via their organizations and clubs: the CBI, Rotary, Lions, etc. If they will only take the trouble to sort out the minimal amount of extra administrative work involved, it is a fairly painless way of raising substantial sums of money.

Much more painful – but perhaps more enjoyable too – are the ideas and effort generated by people who give freely of their time and energy to help. Just in case they might be running out of ideas, here is a fund-raising alphabet compiled by the National Federation of Community Organizations.

A Appeal, Art Exhibition (of members' work), Athletic events or Field Day.
B Baby Sitting, A Ball, Balloon Race, Barbecue, Barn Dance, Beetle Drive, Bingo, Bring & Buy Sale, Bulb Growing Contest.
C Cabaret, Carnival, Car Washing, Charity Cricket Matches, Coffee Mornings, Coins in a Fountain, Concert.
D Dances, Dinner, Double Your Money (each person is given a sum of money and asked to find a way of multiplying it e.g.,

buying a tin of boot polish and starting a shoeshine service.
A prize is given to the most original and/or profitable idea.
This is particularly appropriate for fund-raising by children.)

Dutch Auction (items to be auctioned should be objects
which 'everyone' wants – electrical household goods, etc.
The auctioneer takes one item and asks what he/she is bid.
The first person might say '50p'. The money bid is collected
in a tin. The next person raises the bid to perhaps 80p and
must put the difference, i.e., 30p, into the tin. This process
continues until the auctioneer suddenly says 'sold' at a time
decided in advance and known only to him. The buyer has
then paid out only a small sum (perhaps 40p) for an item
worth very much more, since he only pays the difference
from the last bidding. The attraction of this event is that
anyone who is bidding stands to get the item for a very small
outlay, while the auctioneer can make as much as twenty
times the actual value of the item.)

E Exhibitions, Empties (collecting and returning empty bottles,
for the deposit will not only raise money but will help clean
up the neighbourhood and aid recycling).

F Fairs, Festivals, Fête or Gala, Film Shows, Football Match,
Fortune Telling, Fur and Feather Show, 50–50 Sale (ask
people to contribute nearly new clothes or household articles
in good condition on a 'sale or return' basis. If the item is
sold, half the price is returned to the donor and the other
half is donated to the hospice. It is important that the sale
price should be agreed in advance with the donor and clearly
marked on the item.)

G Garden Parties, Gardening, Go-Karting.

H Halloween Party, Hat Sales, Home Decorations, Home
Made Goods.

I International Evening.

J Jobs about the house, garden or neighbourhood, Jumble
Sales.

L Lawn Mowing, Lecture Service (if any of your members are
regularly invited to give talks to other groups, or lecture in a
voluntary capacity, ask them to request a donation. For
many groups, this is an established way of showing their
gratitude to a speaker.)

M Market Stall, Medieval Banquets or Fairs, Model Making,
Model Railway/Aircraft Exhibitions.

N Nearly New Sale.

O Outings, Outgrown Clothes Sale.

P Pageants, Panel Games, Pantomime, Pile or Jar of Pennies (guess the amount), Plant Sale, Pool Tables, Pram Race, Puppetry, Photo Flash (photographic enthusiasts may take pictures of an event and develop and print them for sale to the subjects. An 'instant' camera allows for instant sales at parties, dances, etc., but the higher price may cut down the profit margin).

Q Quizzes.

R Raffles, Rallies, Record Swaps, Retailing of Goods Bought Wholesale.

S Sale of Work, Secondhand Market, Snowball Tea or Coffee Morning, Sponsored Events, Sports Days, Street Collections, Swimming Gala, Swap Shop.

T Tombola, Toy Making, Trading Stamps, Treasure Hunt.

U Universal Aunts (a group who will do anything and go anywhere – odd jobs, busking, decorating, car washing, dog-walking, baby-sitting, etc. Add a couple of free services like prescription-fetching or shopping for the elderly and infirm to help spread the word about the group – a good activity for a group of younger members.)

V Vegetable Market, Vending Machines, Visit-A-Week/ Month.

W Whist Drives, Window Cleaning, Waste Collection (there is a wide range of waste materials that can be collected and sold for scrap – paper, metal, old clothes, etc. Check the Yellow Pages under Waste Paper and Scrap-Metal Merchants.

Y Your Own Ideas.

Z Zany ideas e.g., bed races, sponsored silences, etc.

For a detailed booklet of fund-raising ideas try *The Community Organization's Survival Kit* (price £1.50 inc. p. & p.) available from the National Federation of Community Organizations, 8 Upper Street, London N1. Tel. 01 226 0189.

Covenants
Straight donations are always welcome but many hospices rely on covenants – a form of regular, annual giving, in which the hospice or charity can recover the income tax on the money given. (This

applies only to tax-payers and the higher the rate of tax you pay, the greater the benefit. The covenant can be paid on whatever date you choose.)

Bequests

Considering the degree of help offered, it is hardly surprising that many patients, relatives and friends choose to leave money to particular hospices or charities in the form of bequests. A typical form of words in a will or codicil might be as follows:

I give the charity known as . . . (name of hospice or charity) of . . . (address) the sum of £—— (free of tax) for its general purposes and I declare that the receipt of the administrator or other duly authorized officer of such charity shall be a sufficient discharge for the same.

And whatever tax-efficient means you might be using to make a donation, be sure to tell the beneficiaries as soon as possible that the money is earmarked for them. It really helps them in their planning.

Details of training courses for charity fund-raisers are obtainable from the Institute of Charity Fundraising Managers, 208–210, Market Towers, 1, Nine Elms Lane, London SW8 5NQ. (Director – Steven Lee). Tel: 01 627 3436.

And from the Directory of Social Change, Radius Works, Back Lane, London NW3 1HL. Tel: 01-435-8171.

12. HOW TO OBTAIN ADMISSION TO A HOSPICE

Your local GP is the main point for referral to a hospice, but a responsible nurse should also be able to refer a patient after making prior arrangements with the doctor. Relatives and/or friends may ask the patient's GP to refer him or her. In a few cases e.g., for Marie Curie nurses to help in the home, or for some AIDS hospices, patients can make the approach themselves.

Referral does not have to wait until intensive terminal care is required. An early approach can ensure that the care is tailored to the patient's needs and reassessed as often as necessary. Referrals can cover the whole range of hospice services – advice on symptom control, home care, a day hospice, in-patient care and bereavement counselling.

Each individual case will almost certainly be discussed by the whole hospice team and their decision will depend not just on what stage the disease has reached but also on the individual circumstances of the patient. They will look not only at the diagnosis and the state of the disease, but also consider the personal wishes of the patient, the degree of support they can expect at home and the advice of the home-care (or primary-care) team. Sometimes an instant decision will be made but such occasions will tend to be the exception rather than the rule. Leaflets and/or brochures explaining admissions policy are usually available from each hospice. And do remember that hospice beds are *not* for geriatric or chronically sick patients.

The assessment to decide the appropriate level of care can be carried out in the patient's own home by a nurse (home-care or hospice-liaison nurse) and/or a physiotherapist or occupational therapist. Such assessments will be updated regularly while the patient remains at home. You can also have the assessment made as an out-patient in the hospice unit. A social worker may also be involved in the full assessment and admission may, in certain circumstances, depend on significant people other than the patient. One alternative to admission may be to improve the facilities available within the patient's home e.g., a telephone, a commode and a suitable bed. And arrangements can usually be made to provide these quickly. Much additional help and advice can be obtained from the appropriate charities, most of whom are just a telephone call away.

13. THE HOSPICE CHARITIES
How They Can Help

Many of the charities listed on the following pages have produced videos about their work; all have brochures and/or regular newsletters and other literature available to give a more detailed account of the help they offer. So far as children's charities are concerned, only the main contacts are included here – the chapter, Hospice Help for Children, contains fuller details.

BACUP

Helps patients, their families and friends cope with cancer. Also answers enquiries on all aspects of cancer from health professionals and the general public. Trained cancer nurses provide information, emotional support and practical advice by telephone or letter. A one-to-one counselling service is available in Greater London. A free, national cancer-information service is now being used by over 500 families every week – and demand is increasing. A video, 'Breaking the Silence on Cancer', is available, and is suitable for support groups, societies, schools, health care and nurses' training programmes – or, indeed, any interested organizations and individuals. It costs £10 to buy; hiring is free of charge, but please send £2.50 to cover postage and packing.

The address is BACUP, 121–3 Charterhouse Street, London EC1M 6AA.

Tel. Cancer Information Service – 01 608 1661 (6 lines).

Information Linkline (outside London) – 0800 181199.

Administration – 01 608 1785.

CANCERLINK

Provides emotional support and information in response to telephone and letter enquiries on all aspects of cancer, from people with cancer, families, friends and professionals working with patients. Acts as a resource to over 300 cancer support and self-help groups throughout Britain, and helps people who are setting up new groups.

The address is CancerLink, 17 Britannia Street, London WC1X 9JN. Tel. 01 833 2451.

Scottish office – 9 Castle Terrace, Edinburgh EH1 2DP. Tel. 031 228 5557.

CANCER RELIEF MACMILLAN FUND

Supports and develops a wide-ranging network of services to provide skilled care for people with cancer and their families. More than 600 Macmillan nurses take a high degree of skill into the patient's own home and help over 45,000 people every year. Macmillan units provide in-patient and day-care facilities which are usually part of the NHS. CRMF has built and equipped fifteen Macmillan Cancer Care Units which are now run by the NHS; it has also part-funded thirteen other building projects, including day-care units (five of which opened in 1988). Financial help e.g., heating, telephone, travelling expenses for treatment, is available through grants (apply through community nurses and hospital or local authority social workers). Two million pounds' worth were distributed in the last financial year. Cancer Relief has also funded fifteen medical and nursing lectureships as well as some fifty nurse tutorships to make the teaching of palliative care (focusing on the quality of life) more widely available. CRMF is the main source of funding for CancerLink, the Breast Care and Mastectomy Association of Great Britain, the British Colostomy Association and the National Association of Laryngectomy Clubs. The number of people those four organizations help each year has passed the 65,000 mark and is continuing to rise rapidly.

The address is Cancer Relief Macmillan Fund, Anchor House, 15–19 Britten Street, London SW3 3TZ. Tel. 01 351 7811.

Scottish office – 9 Castle Terrace, Edinburgh EH1 2DP. Tel. 031 229 3276.

HELP THE HOSPICES

Acts as a voice and pressure group for the hospice movement as a whole. Will fund specific projects, equipment, education and research in the field of terminal care. It runs or supports management policy, counselling and family therapy workshops and clinical courses in this field. It does not support major construction work or the routine costs of established units.

The address is Help the Hospices, BMA House, Tavistock Square, London WC1H 9JP. Tel. 01 388 7807.

THE LISA SAINSBURY FOUNDATION

This provides computerized information and educational help by means of workshops (over 200 a year) for health-care professionals working with the terminally ill. It also publishes numerous, highly relevant books, reading lists on particular topics, lists of videotapes and help agencies. Syringe drivers and portable cassette players are lent on request to meet the needs of specific patients. A newsletter is sent twice a year to everyone on the mailing list.

The address is Lisa Sainsbury Foundation, 8–10 Crown Hill, Croydon, Surrey CRO 1RY. Tel. 01 686 8808.

THE MARIE CURIE MEMORIAL FOUNDATION
(MARIE CURIE CANCER CARE)

The Marie Curie makes enormous contributions to the fight against cancer in four distinct areas: it maintains eleven residential homes throughout the UK, each offering, within its own community area, a very wide range of medical expertise and nursing care (admission details through individual matrons); it provides 4600 Marie Curie nurses who care for patients day and night in their own homes (arranged through the Community Nursing Service, administered by the local health authority); it has a department of education which maintains teaching facilities for medical and nursing professionals in the UK and is increasingly becoming involved in public education; and it funds a well-known research institute which liaises with the other cancer research organizations.

The address is The Marie Curie Memorial Foundation, 28 Belgrave Square, London SW1X 8OQ. Tel. 01 235 3325.

Scottish office – 21 Rutland Street, Edinburgh EH1 2AH. Tel. 031 229 8332.

THE SUE RYDER FOUNDATION

Founded in 1953, the Sue Ryder Foundation works with patients of all ages who have a wide range of disabilities (including Huntington's Chorea) – not just those which are cancer induced. Some of their eighty homes in Britain and overseas have visiting nurses who attend patients in their own homes before admission and after discharge. Seven of the homes in the UK are devoted to the continuing care of cancer patients, both convalescent and terminal. Bereavement counselling is also undertaken. Since its first home was opened, the Foundation has cared for over 56,000 patients in Britain and overseas. Referral to a Sue Ryder home is usually through the patient's own doctor, social worker or radiotherapy centre.

The address is The Sue Ryder Foundation Headquarters, Cavendish, Sudbury, Suffolk CO10 8AY. Tel. 0787 280252.

14. OTHER USEFUL CHARITIES AND CONTACTS

ACT

An umbrella group providing *the* reference point on hospice care for children (see pp. 50–52). Information gathered and sifted on a national basis. Advice given.

Address – Jill Pomerance or Jo Hearn, Institute of Child Health, Royal Hospital for Sick Children, St Michael's Hill, Bristol BS2 8BJ. Tel. 0272 221556/215411, ext 5558.

THE ALDER CENTRE

A nationwide befriending and counselling service for those who have lost a child and desperately need either considerable emotional help or an understanding shoulder to cry on (see p. 36).

Address: c/o Royal Liverpool Children's Hospital, Alder Hey, Eaton Road, Liverpool L12 2AP. Tel. 051 228 4811.

ALZHEIMER'S DISEASE SOCIETY

Raises funds to support hospices.

Address: 3rd Floor, Bank Building, Fulham Broadway, London SW6 1EP. Tel. 01 381 3177.

ASSOCIATION OF CARERS

Organizes self-help groups for carers of disabled and/or elderly dependent relatives. Publishes 'Signpost' guide, *Help at Hand*.

Address: 1st Floor, 21–3 New Road, Chatham, Kent ME4 4JQ. Tel. 0634 813981.

ASSOCIATION OF CHARITY OFFICERS

The place to contact (along with the Hospice Information Service) if you cannot find a suitable organization that can help you.

Address: Association of Charity Officers, c/o RICS Benevolent Fund, 2nd Floor, Tavistock House North, Tavistock Square, London WC1H 9RJ. Tel. 01 387 0578.

ASSOCIATION TO COMBAT HUNTINGTON'S
CHOREA (COMBAT)

Concerned with all aspects of the hereditary disease, Huntington's Chorea. Regional support offices and branches. There is an advice/counselling service and support for patients and their families – and for care professionals too.

Head office: 34a Station Road, Hinckley, Leicestershire LE10 1AP. Tel. 0455 615558.

Family service: 108 Battersea High Street, London SW11 3HP. Tel. 01 223 7000.

Respite care home: Tel. 0378 77588.

ASSOCIATION FOR PALLIATIVE MEDICINE

Formerly the Association of Palliative Care and Hospice Doctors, this is for all doctors working full-time or part-time in hospice-type units in Great Britain and Ireland. Its Hon. Secretary is Dr Anne Naysmith; its Administrative Secretary is Sheila Richards.

Address: Royal South Hants Hospital, Brinton's Terrace, Southampton SO2 0AJ. Tel. 0703 639391.

ASSOCIATION OF HOSPICE ADMINISTRATORS

This is open to the principal administrator in all hospice units and teams. It holds meetings, workshops, an annual conference and produces newsletters. The Secretary is Mr Michael Connolly.

Address: St Anne's Hospice, St Anne's Road North, Heald Green, Cheadle, Cheshire SK8 3SZ. Tel. 061 437 8136.

ASSOCIATION OF HOSPICE CHAPLAINS

For all clergy working full-time, part-time, or occasionally for hospice services. On offer are communication, education and support functions. Annual conferences are planned.

Address: The Rev. Colin Kassell, St Catherine's Hospice, Malthouse Road, Crawley, Sussex RH10 6BH. Tel. 0293 547333.

ASSOCIATION OF HOSPICE SOCIAL WORKERS

This association unites social workers who provide hospice or home-care support. Promotes professional development through an annual workshop and regional meetings, and holds workshops on current issues and talking points. A new secretary is elected annually – the latest contact point can be obtained from the Hospice Information Service (see below).

ASSOCIATION OF HOSPICE VOLUNTARY SERVICE CO-ORDINATORS (SOUTH)

The Association believes in the very important and highly specialized role of volunteers in hospices and is campaigning for their use on a more professional basis. It hopes to have regional branches covering the whole country by the end of 1989. The Association's Hon. Secretary is Brenda Wilkens.

Address: St Catherine's Hospice, Malthouse Road, Crawley, Sussex RH10 6BH. Tel. 0293 547333.

BEREAVED PARENT'S HELPLINE

An organization that gives support to bereaved parents by telephone counselling and home visits.

Address: 6 Canons Gate, Harlow, Essex CM20 1QE. Tel. 0279 412745.

BLISS (BABY LIFE SUPPORT SYSTEMS)

Setting up national network of support groups to help parents of babies in intensive care.

Address: 298 Woodlands Avenue, Eastcote, Ruislip, Middlesex HA4 9QZ. Tel. 01 868 7593.

BREAST CARE AND MASTECTOMY ASSOCIATION OF GREAT BRITAIN

A nationwide free service of practical advice, information and support to women concerned about breast cancer – to complement medical and nursing care. Literature on prostheses, lingerie, swimwear, etc. is available by post (SAE please) – a large selection is usually available at the office (appointment preferred), and there is a list of stockists around the country.

Address: BCMA, 26a Harrison Street, London WC1H 8JG. Tel. 01 837 0908.

Scottish office: 9 Castle Terrace, Edinburgh EH1 2DP. Tel. 031 228 6715.

BRITISH ASSOCIATION FOR COUNSELLING

BAC members are individuals and organizations concerned with counselling. Their information office publishes directories listing counselling services and will refer enquirers to an experienced local counsellor free of charge. If writing, please enclose a SAE.

Address: 37a Sheep Street, Rugby, Warwickshire CV21 3BX. Tel. 0788 78328/9.

BRITISH COLOSTOMY ASSOCIATION

An information and advisory service, giving comfort, reassurance and encouragement to patients to return to their previous active lifestyle. Emotional support is given on a confidential basis by helpers who have long experience of living with a colostomy. A list of contacts is available for each area. Visits in hospitals or at home can be arranged on request.

Address: 38–9 Eccleston Square, London SW1V 1PB. Tel. 01 828 5175.

BRITISH LIBRARY OF TAPE RECORDINGS FOR HOSPITAL PATIENTS

Tape-recorded books for the use of patients who, because of illness or any type of therapy, cannot read. Check first to make sure the patient has access to a suitable playback machine.

Address: 12 Lant Street, London SE1 1QR. Tel. 01 407 9417/8.

BRITISH SOCIETY FOR MUSIC THERAPY

Promotes the use and development of music therapy in treatment, education, rehabilitation and training of adults and children suffering from emotional, physical or mental handicap.

Address: 69 Avondale Avenue, East Barnet, Hertfordshire EN4 8NB.

THE BUDDHIST HOSPICE TRUST

Formed in 1986 to explore the relationship between the teachings of the Buddha and the philosophy of hospice care. It provides physical care, emotional support and spiritual counselling for those who are bereaved and works closely with the hospice movement.

Address: Dennis Sibley, 17 Cavendish Place, Newport, Isle of Wight PO30 5AE.

CAMP QUALITY UK

Offers free holidays in Britain to children with cancer, leukaemia and other life-threatening illnesses. More details in the chapter on Hospice Help for Children, p. 57.

Address: Mrs Earline Campbell, 1 The Mews, Umberslade Hall, Tanworth-in-Arden, Warwickshire B94 5DF. Tel. 05644 2098.

CANCER AFTERCARE & REHABILITATION SOCIETY (CARE)

An organization of cancer patients formed into self-help groups which offer advice and support. Forty-seven branches and contacts throughout the country provide social outlets as well as informative activities.

Address: 21 Zetland Road, Redland, Bristol BS6 7AH. Tel. 0272 427419.

CANCER RESEARCH CAMPAIGN

Can advise on research funding of cancer projects and education about cancer and its psychological effects.

Address: 2 Carlton House Terrace, London SW1V 5AR. Tel. 01 930 8972.

CARERS' NATIONAL ASSOCIATION

An information and advice service for those whose life is restricted because of their need to care for the ill or the disabled. Local groups can put carers in touch with each other. Encourages self-help and lobbies government, both local and national, on behalf of carers.

Address: 29 Chilworth Mews, London W2 3RG. Tel. 01 724 7776.

CENTRE FOR ATTITUDINAL HEALING

Support groups with weekly meetings for people with serious diseases; there are four in London, one in Southsea – more are planned.

Address: 31 Craven Street, London WC2N 5NP. Tel. 01 839 3087.

CHILDREN'S CANCER HELP CENTRE

Aims to relieve the sickness and suffering of any person, particularly children, who have cancer or a life-threatening illness, and their families. Emphasis is placed on counselling and healing; also some relaxation and visualization.

Address: 14 Kingsway, Petts Wood, Orpington, Kent. Tel. 0689 35455.

CLIC

Cancer and Leukaemia in Childhood provides extra back-up to ease the difficulties of families with very sick children (see p. 53). At present it operates only in the south-west of England (where it began and where it has considerable support); but other parts of Britain have expressed interest in working with the ideas of CLIC's founder, Dr Bob Woodward.

Address: CLIC House, 11–12 Fremantle Square, Cotham, Bristol BS6 5TL. Tel. 0272 48844.

COPE (UK)

Aims to develop neighbourhood support for families, to provide opportunities to learn basic skills for those caring for dependents, and to provide leisure breaks for adults and children.

Address: 8th Floor, 19–29 Woburn Place, London WC1H 0LY. Tel. 01 278 7048.

THE COMPASSIONATE FRIENDS

A self-help group of parents who have lost a son or daughter of any age, including adult (see p. 40).

Address: 6 Denmark Street, Bristol BS1 5DQ. Tel. 0272 292778.

COUNCIL FOR MUSIC IN HOSPITALS

Organizes live concerts by professional musicians in hospices, hospitals and homes throughout the UK.

Address: 340 Lower Road, Little Bookham, Surrey KT23 4EF. Tel. 0372 58264.

COUNSEL AND CARE FOR THE ELDERLY

Offers a free advisory service to all elderly people and to professionals. Some financial help is available. Every year it inspects all registered private residential homes in Greater London.

Address: Twyman House, 16 Bonny Street, London NW1 9LR.
Tel. (Administration): 01 485 1550.
(Appeals): 01 485 5413.
(Casework 10.30am – 4pm): 01 485 1566.

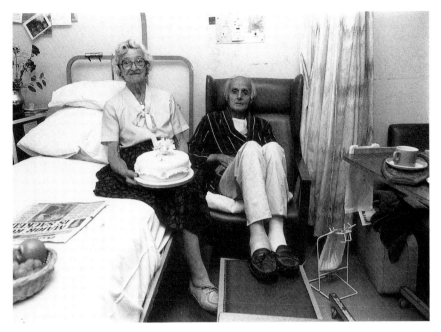

Jack Thompson (cancer prostate) celebrating his Golden
Wedding anniversary with his wife.

Agnes Upcraft (glioma) being visited by her two sons.

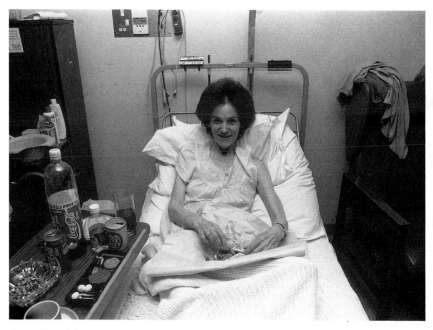

Anna (Annie) Hopwood (cancer of the cervix) as an inpatient.

Anna (Annie) Hopwood with daughters Caroline and Miriam at home after being told she is cured.

CROSSROADS (ASSOCIATION OF CROSSROADS CARE
ATTENDANT SCHEME)

Has schemes in various parts of the country in which handicapped people can be cared for in their own homes, by people they know and trust, to allow their families to have a break.

Address: 94 Coton Road, Rugby, Warwickshire CV21 4LN. Tel. 0788 73653.

CRUSE

A national organization to help any bereaved person (see p. 40).

Address: Cruse House, 126 Sheen Road, Richmond, Surrey TW9 1UR. Tel. 01 940 4818.

DISABLED LIVING FOUNDATION

Offers an information service for disabled people, carers and professionals, by letter and telephone. Specialist advisory services on clothing and footwear, incontinence, music and visual handicap. Reference library stocks 6000 books and pamphlets, 300 current journals on all (non-medical) aspects of disability. Publications include resource papers, reading lists and comprehensive lists of equipment for disability.

Address: 380 Harrow Road, London W9 2HU. Tel. 01 289 6111.

EDWARDS SYNDROME SOCIETY

Offers support, help and comfort for children with Edwards Syndrome and their families, and for families of those children who have died. Has a regular newsletter.

Address: 3 Devon Close, Perivale, Greenford, Middlesex UB6 7DM. Tel. 01 998 4126.

FAMILY WELFARE ASSOCIATION

Offers a professional casework and counselling service for families in distress; also makes grants and publishes leaflets.

Address: 501–5 Kingsland Road, London E8 4AU. Tel. 01 254 6251.

FOUNDATION FOR BLACK BEREAVED
FAMILIES

Offers help and support for bereaved black people of Afro-

Caribbean origin. Counselling, advice, home visits, funeral attendance and financial support.

Address: 11 Kingston Hill, Salters Hill, London SE19 1DZ. Tel. 01 761 7228.

HEADWAY – NATIONAL HEAD INJURIES ASSOCIATION

Supports and advises the families of patients suffering from severe head injuries and those recovering from head/brain surgery. Through support groups, it aims to offer activities to help rehabilitation and create social outlets.

Address: 200 Mansfield Road, Nottingham NG1 3HX. Tel. 0602 622383.

HODGKIN'S DISEASE ASSOCIATION

Provides information and emotional support for lymphoma (Hodgkin's Disease and non-Hodgkin's lymphoma) patients and their families. There is a national network of helpers with experience of the disease, with whom enquirers can be linked, usually by telephone.

Address: PO Box 275, Haddenham, Aylesbury, Buckinghamshire HP17 8JJ. Tel. 0844 291500.

HOMELINK

A small local service run by volunteers in Sevenoaks in Kent, but included because of its similarity to other services growing up around the country (enquire locally). The volunteers 'sit in' with handicapped or sick people to relieve the home carer (to allow them to go shopping, etc.) They also offer help to those who are lonely or have difficulty using public transport. They are also always on the lookout for new volunteers.

Address (for Sevenoaks area only): Mrs Jill Webster, Volunteer Bureau, 34 Buckhurst Avenue, Sevenoaks, Kent. Tel. 0732 454785.

HOSPICE ARTS

The encouragement of arts in hospices (see p. 73).

Address: Forbes Trust, 9 Artillery Lane, London EC1 7LP. Tel. 01 377 8484.

HOSPICE INFORMATION SERVICE

The clearing house for everything you ever wanted to know about the hospice movement in Britain and overseas. Avril Jackson and Ann Eve keep their files and contacts bang up-to-date. And if by some chance they cannot give you an answer, they will tell you how to get in touch with someone who can.

Address: St Christopher's Hospice, 51–9 Lawrie Park Road, London SE26 6DZ. Tel. 01 778 9252.

HOSPICE NURSE MANAGERS' FORUM

This is a forum of the management Association of the Royal College of Nursing of the United Kingdom. Its purpose is to provide opportunities for nurses engaged in hospice management to meet together to discuss developments and matters of common interest. The Secretary is Mrs Bronwen Biswas.

Address: The Leicestershire Hospice, Groby Road Hospital, Leicester LE3 9QB. Tel. 0533 313771.

HYSTERECTOMY SUPPORT

Refers women (and family or partners) concerned about hysterectomy to former patients in their area who will provide encouragement, advice and support through the informal sharing of experiences and information. Membership of local support groups is available. Contact can be by letter, over the telephone or at group meetings.

Address: c/o WHRIC, 52 Featherstone Street, London EC1Y 8RT. Tel. (11am–5pm weekdays except Tuesday) 01 251 6332/6580.

INSTITUTE FOR COMPLEMENTARY MEDICINE

Can supply names of reliable practitioners of complementary medicine, such as homeopathy, relaxation techniques and osteopathy. Also has contact with other support groups. Please send SAE for information, indicating area of interest.

Address: 21 Portland Place, London W1N 3AF. Tel. 01 693 9543.

INSTITUTE OF FAMILY THERAPY

The Institute's Elizabeth Raven Memorial Fund offers free counselling to bereaved families or those who have a seriously ill family member. While the service is free, voluntary donations to the fund are accepted to help other families.

Address: 43 New Cavendish Street, London W1M 7RG. Tel. 01 935 1651.

THE INTERNATIONAL SCHOOL FOR CANCER CARE

Registered charity facilitating the training of health-care workers worldwide in palliative care of cancer patients. Travelling fellow-ships, conference bursaries, workshops and project assistance are available. The Chairman is Dr. R.G. Twycross; Director is Mrs Gillian Hunter.

Address: Royal Marsden Hospital, Fulham Road, London SW3 6JJ. Tel. 01 376 3623.

IRISH CANCER SOCIETY

Information on all aspects of cancer from nurses via freefone service. The society funds home-care and rehabilitation pro-grammes run by voluntary groups for all cancer patients. There are support groups for mastectomy, colostomy and laryngectomy patients; advice too on Hodgkin's Disease. A home night-nursing service is available at the request of the patient's doctor or the public-health nurse.

Address: Information Officer, Irish Cancer Society, 5 North-umberland Road, Dublin 4. Tel. (Ireland only) 0001 681855 *or* dial 10 and ask for 'Freefone Cancer'.

JEWISH BEREAVEMENT COUNSELLING SERVICE

Will send trained volunteer counsellors to the bereaved; they will visit weekly as long as necessary. Operates in Greater London but can refer to other projects and individuals who help deal with bereavement in other parts of the country.

Address: 1 Cyprus Gardens, London N3 1SP. Tel. 01 349 0839 and 01 387 4300, ext. 227.

LET'S FACE IT

A contact point for people of any age coping with facial disfigurement following an operation. Provides a link for people with similar experiences. Telephone and letter contact; meetings for self-help or social contact.

Address: Christine Piff, 10 Wood End, Crowthorne, Berkshire RG11 6DQ. Tel. 0344 774405.

LEUKAEMIA CARE SOCIETY

Promotes the welfare of people with leukaemia and allied blood disorders. Offers family caravan holidays, friendship and support through unpaid area secretaries around Great Britain. Limited financial assistance is available. Membership is free.

Address: PO Box 82, Exeter, Devon EX2 5DP. Tel. 0392 218514.

LONDON BEREAVEMENT PROJECTS CO-ORDINATING GROUP

Umbrella organization for over thirty bereavement projects in London and the Home Counties. Offers counselling and visiting service for anyone who is bereaved.

Address: 68 Chalton Street, London NW1 1HY. Tel. 01 388 0241.

THE MALCOLM SARGENT CANCER FUND FOR CHILDREN

Can provide cash grants for parents of children up to the age of twenty-one with cancer, to help pay for clothing, equipment, travel, fuel, bills, etc. Apply through a hospital social worker anywhere in the UK. Grants approved within twenty-four hours.

Address: 14 Abingdon Road, London W8 6AF. Tel. 01 937 4548.

MARY WARD CENTRE

Offers a 'Creative Response to Cancer' course of ten two-hour sessions to release the power of the imagination in drawing, writing, talking, relaxation and visualization to help cancer sufferers learn to come to terms with fear and despair.

Address: 42 Queen Square, London WC1 3AQ.

MEDICAL ADVISORY SERVICE

A telephone service, run by nurses, offering information and advice on medical and health-care matters, putting people in touch with the right organization.

Address: 10 Barley Mow Passage, London W4 4PH. Tel. 01 994 9874 (7am–10pm, Mon–Fri).

MOTOR-NEURONE DISEASE ASSOCIATION

Advice and information for those affected. Regional care advisers will visit. Financial grants to help ensure that patients are looked after, either in their own home or a hospice while their regular carers take a break. Free loan of various aids, including elevating and reclining chairs, bed elevators, communication devices and suction units. Discretionary grants to provide additional training for hospice staff in the care of people with MND. Over sixty locally based branches raise funds and provide help and support. Volunteers available for home visits.

Address: 61 Derngate, Northampton NN1 1UE. Tel. 0604 250505 (24-hour tel. 0604 22269).

MULTIPLE SCLEROSIS TELEPHONE COUNSELLING SERVICE

Run under the auspices of ARMS (Action for Research in MS), it offers a listening ear, help and information for all who have multiple sclerosis and for those near them. It is manned by trained counsellors available on the following numbers:

London: 01 568 2255
Glasgow: 041 6372262
Birmingham: 021 4764229
N. Ireland: 0247 63378

NATIONAL AIDS TRUST

Helps raise money to fund the development of AIDS hospices and other AIDS-related projects, and has access to a stable of experts who are up-to-date with the latest developments.

Address: 33 Holborn, London EC1P 1DQ. Tel. 01 822 3209/ 2219/2000.

NATIONAL ASSOCIATION OF LARYNGECTOMY CLUBS

Promotes the welfare of laryngectomees within the British Isles. Encourages the formation of clubs (almost seventy affiliated so far) with the objective of assisting rehabilitation through speech therapy, social support and monthly meetings. Advises on speech aids and medical supplies and offers a referral service.

Address: 4th Floor, 39 Eccleston Square, London SW1V 1PB. Tel. 01 834 2857.

NATIONAL COUNCIL FOR CARERS AND THEIR
ELDERLY DEPENDANTS

Free information and guidance service (benefits, holiday relief) for those looking after elderly or infirm relatives.

Address: 29 Chilworth Mews, London W2 3RG. Tel. 01 262 1451.

NEW APPROACHES TO CANCER

A clearing house for information and advice on a range of complementary therapies. A register of practitioners and therapists is available.

Address: The Seekers' Trust, Addington Park, Maidstone, Kent ME19 5BL. Tel. 0732 848336.

THE NEUROBLASTOMA SOCIETY

Offers information and advice by telephone or letter for patients and their families. Provides contact, for mutual support, with others who have experienced the illness in the family.

Address: Neville & Janet Oldridge, Woodlands, Ordsall Park Road, Retford, Nottinghamshire DN22 7PJ. Tel. 0777 709238.

OESOPHAGEAL PATIENTS' ASSOCIATION

Leaflets, telephone advice and support before and during drug treatment. Visits, where possible, by former patients to people with oesophageal cancer.

Address: 16 Whitefields Crescent, Solihull, West Midlands B91 3NU. Tel. 021 704 9860.

PARKINSON'S DISEASE SOCIETY OF THE UK

Has about 130 branches in the UK. Provides list of contact addresses for support to families and sufferers of Parkinson's Disease. Produces information, leaflets and a newsletter. Promotes research.

Address: 36 Portland Place, London W1N 3DG. Tel. 01 323 1174.

PROFESSIONAL CLASSES' AID COUNCIL

Aims to relieve distress among professional men and women and their dependants by making continuing grants and gifts for maintenance, special needs and, in certain cases, education and training. Advice given about other sources of help.

Address: 10 St Christopher's Place, London W1M 6HY. Tel. 01 935 0641.

PRUE CLENCH

Pioneer founder of the Dorothy House Foundation in Bath, a recognized model of community hospice care, Mrs Prue Clench MBE, SRN is now a nurse adviser on the setting up and development of terminal-care services.

Address: 'Tamarisk', 6 Clinton Drive, St Austell, Cornwall. Tel. 0726 74691.

QUEST FOR A TEST FOR CANCER

Quest carries out unique non-animal research to try to develop routine cancer testing for everyone, by assessing the initial changes in cells before a cancerous tumour or abnormality develops – something that body scanners and mammography cannot do. Significant progress has been made with the development of a test which has had a preliminary trial at London's Middlesex Hospital. This test has now been applied successfully to cervical and breast cancer and work is continuing on developing similar tests for lung, thyroid, colon and testicular cancers. Quest is also investigating the hereditary factor in families prone to cancer and those cancers which particularly affect children.

Address: Mrs Jean Pitt, Woodbury, Harlow Road, Roydon, Essex CM19 5HF. Tel. 027979 3678/2233.

RCN (ASSOCIATION OF NURSING PRACTICE)
SYMPTOM CONTROL & CARE OF THE DYING FORUM

This provides a forum for nurses who provide hospice services; sets out to encourage 'professional and political awareness' and aims to make it easier to provide a corporate response to professional issues. The Chairman is Barbara Dicks.

Address: North-East Thames Regional Health Authority, 40 Eastbourne Terrace, London W2 3QR. Tel. 01 262 8011.

RED CROSS MEDICAL LOANS SERVICE

Branches around the country provide medical equipment on loan for short periods for patients living at home. This also includes walking sticks, wheelchairs and commodes. For the address and telephone number, look in your local phone book.

RETINOBLASTOMA SOCIETY

Links families in the same situation and area to give moral support and practical help. Creates an opportunity for parents to exchange information and share experiences.

Address: Mrs Kay Balmforth, Childrens Dept, Moorfields Eye Hospital, City Road, London EC1V 2PD. Tel. 01 253 3411, ext. 2345.

ROYAL COLLEGE OF RADIOLOGISTS

Celebrating their golden jubilee in European Cancer year, these experts at the heart of certain types of cancer treatment have recently launched a campaign to try to dispel the image of 'gloom and doom'. The College is at pains to emphasize that many people *are* helped and that treatments are often far less traumatic than is believed.

Address: 38 Portland Place, London W1N 3DG. Tel. 01 636 4432.

THE SAMARITANS

They offer emotional support and befriending to the lonely, suicidal and despairing. For the telephone number look in your local phone book under 'S' or on the emergency page.

SAVE OUR SONS

Information and emotional support for men and boys with testicular cancer. Advice given by qualified nurse who will listen and offer help wherever possible. A leaflet is available on self-examination techniques.

Address: Shirley Wilcox, Tides Reach, 1 Kite Hill, Wooton Bridge, Isle of Wight PO33 4LA. Tel. 0983 882876 (evenings preferred).

SHARE-A-CARE

If you, or someone you care for, has an uncommon illness and you would like to talk about it with someone who suffers from the same thing, please write, enclosing a stamp.

Address: 8 Cornmarket, Faringdon, Oxfordshire.

TAK TENT

An organization that brings together cancer patients, their families and members of the caring team. A participation group providing a friendly environment where all concerned can share their experiences and learn from them.

Address: 132 Hill Street, Glasgow. Tel. 041 332 3639.

TENOVUS CANCER INFORMATION CENTRE

Although the primary concern is prevention, the Centre provides information and advice on all cancer-related concerns and can refer you to the appropriate cancer organizations for further help.

Address: 142 Whitchurch Road, Cardiff CF4 3NA. Tel. 0222 619846.

THE ULSTER CANCER FOUNDATION

This is involved in many aspects of cancer, from prevention to patient support. The Foundation operates an information helpline for cancer-related queries from patients and their families, staffed by experienced cancer nurses who can arrange counselling. Rehabilitation-support services include mastectomy advice (volunteer visiting by former patients); laryngectomy club (monthly activities, support in hospitals and at home); lymphoma support (patient and family link-up).

Address: 40–42 Eglantine Avenue, Belfast BT9 6DX. Tel. 0232 663281/2/3. Helpline (weekdays, 9.30am–12.30pm) – 0232 663439.

UROSTOMY ASSOCIATION

Assists patients before and after surgery with counselling on appliances, housing, work situations or marital problems. Helps them to resume as full a life as possible. Branch and house meetings are held. Hospital and home visits by former patients can be arranged on request.

Address: 'Buckland', Beaumont Park, Danbury, Essex CM3 4DE. Tel. 024 5414294.

WOMEN'S NATIONAL CANCER CONTROL CAMPAIGN

WNCCC was formed in 1965 to help women overcome their fears about cancer and take simple precautions which could well save their lives. It produces a wide range of literature about cervical smears and breast self-examination. Audio-visual presentations are shown to audiences all over Britain. There are several mobile clinics, screening women at their place of work and in local shopping centres, thus reaching those who find it difficult or inconvenient to attend the usual health clinics. The Campaign also acts as an information centre for women, providing details of *all* screening services. There are some ten branches around the country.

Address: 1 South Audley Street, London W1Y 5DQ. Tel. 01 499 7532/4.

CONCLUSION

In 1980 a special committee of experts reported to the government on the subject of terminal care (The Wilkes Report (DHSS)). It came straight to the point:

We believe that the unmet need in the field of terminal care presents us with an immediate problem. Where the dying are concerned there is, of course, no possibility of trying harder next time. The dead cannot complain and, despite their resentment and grief, the bereaved do so with surprising rarity.

Much has been done in the last decade. The British hospice movement is the example which the rest of the world seeks to follow, beating a path to our door for a place at international conferences, hungry for every new development, for every exchange of ideas. But too many cancer patients, and those with other life-threatening illnesses, still die in hospitals where the emphasis is largely on cure rather than care. It does not have to be so – and, of course, the situation is changing. But that change takes time and has two great obstacles: firstly, the lethargy with which a great many doctors and other medical professionals are embracing the idea of palliative care – it is a concept that, although making great strides, has barely scratched the surface of medical opinion. Remedying that is a major priority for the 1990s.

The second obstacle is the enormous disparity in government help for different hospices in different parts of the country. A few are funded 100 per cent; some get nothing at all; most lie somewhere in between. This disparity is a product of history, of budget priorities, of local health-authority attitudes. Government ministers have publicly accepted the need to address this problem and there are some signs that they will find the money to do so soon. But *few* in the hospice movement seriously suggest that the government pick up the *entire* bill – the element of charitable fund-raising gives the local community an important feeling of involvement and *responsibility* that binds it closer to its hospice. The hospices argue, however, that there should be an official safety net, a minimum level of official funding below which no hospice should ever sink. There is general agreement that the level at which this should be pitched is of crucial psychological importance. Forty-nine per cent is what most hospices would like, as they fear 50 per cent or over might risk encouraging the public to feel that 'the hospices are all right now', with a subsequent reduction in the amount of money coming their way from charitable sources.

To remedy those huge disparities in funding would give the expanding hospice movement a confidence and a sureness of footing that would speed it on its way into the twenty-first century, and be the best possible reward for the pioneering spirit and achievements of a movement that believes the last weeks and months are every bit as precious as the first – that everyone has the right to leave this life with as much care, love and devotion as when they came into it.

Further Reading

A more detailed list, including numerous specialist pamphlets and booklets, is available from the Hospice Information Service at St Christopher's (see p. 99) and from the Lisa Sainsbury Foundation (see p. 89).

Bereavement by C.M. Parkes, pub. Penguin, 1975.

Cicely Saunders – The Founder of the Modern Hospice Movement by S. du Boulay, pub. Hodder & Stoughton, 1984.

Coping with a Dying Relative by D. Doyle, pub. W. & R. Chambers, 1985.

Dying by J. Hinton, pub. Penguin, 1967.

Hospice Care, Principles and Practice by C.A. Corr and D.M. Corr (eds), pub. Springer Publishing Co., New York, 1983.

The Hospice Movement in Britain; Its Role and Its Future by H. Taylor, pub. The Centre for Policy on Ageing, Nuffield Lodge Studio, Regent's Park, London NW1 4RS, 1983.

Life Before Death by A. Cartwright, L. Hockey and J.Z. Anderson, pub. Routledge & Kegan Paul, 1973.

Managing to Care by P. Clench, pub. Patten Press, Hayle, Cornwall, 1984.

On Death and Dying by E. Kubler-Ross, pub. Tavistock Publications, 1970.

St Christopher's in Celebration (21 years at Britain's First Modern Hospice) by C. Saunders (ed.), pub. Hodder & Stoughton, 1988.

Terminal Care – Report of a Working Group (Chairman, Eric Wilkes) by Standing Medical Advisory Committee, pub. HMSO, 1980.

HOSPICE DIRECTORY

The first part of the following index indicates county by county which towns and cities offer some kind of hospice service.

The second, and main, part (p. 119) lists those towns and cities in alphabetical order and indicates the name, address and telephone number of the hospice or home-care team. Initials below each entry show the type of services provided – the key is given on p. 119. Details vary but there is always a contact name, address and telephone number.

Telephone numbers change and new services come on stream so, in case of difficulty, please contact the Hospice Information Service (p. 40). They provide regular amendments and updates several times a year. The list of contacts that follows is based on the annual *Directory of Hospice Services* they produce for the Cancer Relief Macmillan Fund but includes modifications arising from the *Hospice Handbook*'s own survey.

Every effort has been made to ensure that the following directory contains no errors or omissions. The author apologizes to any hospice services or charities which might have slipped through the net and would ask them to write to him personally c/o the Hospice Information Service.

County List

ENGLAND

AVON
Bath – The Dorothy House Foundation
Bristol – St Peter's Hospice

BEDFORDSHIRE
Luton – Luton and Dunstable Hospital, Symptom Control Team
Marsh Farm Health Clinic, Macmillan Service
Moggerhanger – Sue Ryder Home
Shefford – The Health Centre Macmillan Service
Streatley – Luton and South Bedfordshire Hospice

BERKSHIRE
Newbury, Reading & Wokingham – West Berkshire Cancer Care Project
Newbury – Newbury and District Cancer Care Trust
Thatcham Health Centre Macmillan Service
Reading – Dellwood Hospital Macmillan Service
Slough – The Health Clinic Macmillan Service

Sunninghill – The Paul Bevan Cancer
Foundation
Windsor – Thames Valley Hospice
Wokingham – Wokingham Hospital
Macmillan Service

BUCKINGHAMSHIRE

Aylesbury – Aylesbury Vale Hospice
Project
Beaconsfield – The Iain Rennie Hospice
at Home
The South Bucks Hospice – Universal
Hospice Trust
Marlow – Marlow Hospital – Wycombe
Macmillan Service
Milton Keynes – The Hospice of Our
Lady & St John, Willen

CAMBRIDGESHIRE

Cambridge – Arthur Rank House
Milton – Cambridge Children's Hospice
Peterborough – Peterborough Distric
Hospital – Macmillan Service
Peterborough Health Authority
Wisbech – Fenland Hospice and Day
Hospice

CHESHIRE

Cheadle – St Ann's Hospice
Chester – Hospice of the Good
Shepherd
Crewe – The Clinic Centre – Macmillan
Service
Macclesfield – The East Cheshire
Hospice
Warrington – Garven Place Clinic –
Macmillan Service
St Rocco's Hospice
Winsford – St Luke's (Cheshire)
Hospice

CLEVELAND

Guisborough – Guisborough Health
Centre – Macmillan Service
Hartlepool – Hartlepool Hospice
Middlesbrough – Teesside Hospice Care
Foundation
Stockton-on-Tees – Butterwick Hospice
Fairfield Clinic – Macmillan Service

CORNWALL

Hayle – St Julia's Hospice
St Austell – Mount Edgcumbe Hospice
Truro – Macmillan Service

CUMBRIA

Barrow in Furness – Fairfield Clinic –
Macmillan Service
Carlisle – Carlisle and District Hospice
Appeal
Central Clinic – Macmillan Service
Cockermouth – West Cumbria Hospice
at Home
Kendal – Blackhall Road Health Centre
– Macmillan Service
Ulverston – St Mary's Hospice in
Furness
Ulverston Health Centre – Macmillan
Service
Whitehaven – West Cumberland
Hospital
Workington – Ann Burrow Thomas
Health Centre – Macmillan Service

DERBYSHIRE

Bakewell – The Cottage Hospital –
Macmillan Service
Chapel-en-le-Frith – High Peak Hospice
Chesterfield – Ashgate Hospice
Saltergate Health Centre – Macmillan
Service
Derby – Nightingale Macmillan
Continuing Care Unit
Risley – The Draycott Hospice

DEVON

Barnstaple – Hospice Care Trust –
North Devon
Budleigh Salterton – Budleigh Salterton
& District Hospiscare
Exeter – Mowbray Cottage –
Hospiscare
Exmouth – Exmouth Hospital –
Macmillan Service
Plymouth – St Luke's Hospice
Sidmouth – Sidmouth Hospiscare
Tiverton – Tidcombe Hall Marie Curie
Home
Torquay – Castle Circus Health Service
– Macmillan Service
Rowcroft House Foundation

DORSET

Bournemouth – Poole Hospice Project
Christchurch – Christchurch Hospital
Dorchester – Macmillan Service
Wareham – Wareham Health Centre –
Macmillan Service

DURHAM

Chester-le-Street – Chester-le-Street
  Health Centre – Macmillan Service
Consett – North West Durham
  Macmillan Service
Coundon – Health Centre Macmillan
  Service
Darlington – St Theresa's Hospice
  Project
Durham – St Cuthbert's Hospice
Lanchester – Maiden Law Hospital –
  Macmillan Service
Peterlee – Peterlee Child Health Centre
  Macmillan Service

ESSEX

Basildon – Basildon Hospital –
  Macmillan Service
  St Luke's Hospice
Chelmsford – Chelmsford Hospice
Colchester – Macmillan Service
  St Helena Hospice
Epping – St Margaret's Hospital –
  Macmillan Service
  West Essex Hospice Project
Harlow – Princess Alexandra Hospital
Ilford – Manford Way Health Centre –
  Macmillan Service
Romford – St Francis Hospice
Westcliff-on-Sea – Fair Havens

GLOUCESTERSHIRE

Chalford Hill – The Cotswold Care
  Project
Cheltenham – The Health Centre
  Macmillan Service
  Sue Ryder Home, Leckhampton Court
Gloucester – Gloucester Macmillan
  Nursing Service

HAMPSHIRE

Andover – Countess of Brecknock
  House, Andover War Memorial
  Hosp.
Basingstoke – Basingstoke District
  Hospital – Macmillan Service
Lymington – Milford Hospital –
  Macmillan Service
Petersfield – Sue Ryder Home, Bordean
  House
Portsmouth – Portsmouth Area Hospice
  Appeal Fund
Southampton – Countess Mountbatten
  House

HEREFORD

Bartestree – St Michael's Hospice
Tarrington – Hospice of the Marches

HERTFORDSHIRE

Barnet – Barnet General Hospital –
  Barnet Support Team
Berkhamsted – The Hospice of St
  Francis (Berkhamsted)
Chorleywood – Thorpedale Trust
Hemel Hempstead – Hemel Hempstead
  General Hospital – Macmillan
  Service
Hitchin – Hitchin Hospital – Macmillan
  Service
Letchworth – The North Hertfordshire
  Hospice
St Albans – St Albans City Hospital –
  Hospice Home-Care Team
Stevenage – The Lister Hospital
Welwyn Garden City – Hospice Care
  Service for East Hertfordshire

HUMBERSIDE

Grimsby – District General Hospital –
  Support Sister
  St Andrew's Hospice
Holme on Spalding Moor – Sue Ryder
  Home, Hole Holme Hall
Hull – Hull Royal Infirmary –
  Macmillan Service
  North Humberside Hospice Project
Scunthorpe – Scunthorpe & District
  Hospice Appeal (Lindsey Lodge)
  The Support Nurses, Community
  Health Department

ISLE OF WIGHT

Newport – Earl Mountbatten House

KENT

Broadstairs – Broadstairs Health Centre
  – Macmillan Service
Canterbury – Pilgrims Hospice
Dartford – Ellenor Foundation
Edenbridge – Sevenoaks Hospice Link
Herne Bay – The Buddhist Hospice
  Trust
  Queen Victoria Memorial Hospital –
  Macmillan Service
Maidstone – Maidstone Hospice
  Maidstone Hospital – Macmillan
  Service
Meopham – Lions Hospice

Orpington – South Bromley Hospiscare
Rochester – Wisdom Hospice
Sidcup – Bexley Macmillan Support
   Team, Queen Mary's Hospital
Tunbridge Wells – Hospice at Home
   (The Care Foundation)
Welling – Greenwich and Bexley
   Cottage Hospice

LANCASHIRE

Ashton Under Lyne – Tameside General
   Hospital – Macmillan Service
Blackburn – East Lancashire Hospice
Blackpool – Trinity – The Hospice in
   the Fylde
   Victoria Hospital – Macmillan Service
Bolton – Bolton Hospice
   Hulton Hospital – Macmillan Service
Burnley – Burnley General Hospital –
   Macmillan Service
   Hospice Care for Burnley & Pendle
Bury – A Hospice for Bury Association
   Macmillan Service, The Community
   Nursing Office
Lancaster – St John's Hospice
Leigh – Wigan Hospice (Leigh Home
   Care)
Leyland – Leyland Clinic – Macmillan
   Service
Ormskirk – Hettinga House
   Ormskirk & District General Hospital
   – Macmillan Service
Preston – St Catherine's Hospice
Rossendale – Hospice in Rossendale
Wigan – Wigan Hospice

LEICESTERSHIRE

Ashby-de-la-Zouch – Sue Ryder Home,
   Staunton Harold Hall
Hinckley – Hinckley Health Centre –
   Macmillan Service
Leicester – Blaby Hospital – Macmillan
   Service
   Coalville Health Centre – Macmillan
   Service
   Leicester General Hospital –
   Macmillan Service
   The Leicestershire Hospice
   LOROS Day Care Centre
Loughborough – Loughborough Health
   Centre – Macmillan Service
Market Harborough – The Cottage
   Hospital – Macmillan Service
Melton Mowbray – War Memorial
   Hospital – Macmillan Service
Oakham – Rutland Memorial Hospital
   – Macmillan Service

LINCOLNSHIRE

Boston – Boston Health Clinic –
   Macmillan Service
Grantham – Grantham Health Clinic –
   Macmillan Service
   Grantham Hospital – Macmillan
   Service
Lincoln – St Barnabas Hospice

LONDON – EAST

The London Hospital – Macmillan
   Support Team
Mildmay Mission Hospital
St Joseph's Hospice
Whipps Cross Hospital – The Margaret
   Centre

LONDON – EAST-CENTRAL

St Bartholomew's Hospital – Support
   Care Team

LONDON – NORTH

Lordship Lane Clinic – Macmillan
   Service
The North London Hospice
North Middlesex Hospital – Community
   Liaison Sisters
Ridge House Clinic – Continuing Care
   Support Team
Whittington Hospital – Islington
   Support Team

LONDON – NORTH-WEST

Edenhall Marie Curie Home, Hampstead
National Temperance Hospital –
   Bloomsbury Community Care Team
   Bloomsbury Support Team
Royal Free Hospital – Palliative Care/
   Support Team
Hospital of St John & St Elizabeth –
   Catherine McAuley Unit

LONDON – SOUTH-EAST

Greenwich Macmillan Support Team
Guy's Hospital – Guy's Support Team
Hither Green Hospital – Macmillan
   Support Team (Lewisham)
King's College Hospital – Pain Relief
   Unit
St Christopher's Hospice
St Giles Hospital – Camberwell
   Macmillan Continuing Care Team
St Thomas's Hospital – Richard
   Dimbleby Day Centre

LONDON – SOUTH WEST

Brompton Hospital Support Team
The Royal Marsden Hospital –
 Continuing Care Unit
St George's Hospital – Support Team,
 Oncology Unit
Trinity Hospice
Westminster Hospital – Oncology
 Nursing Area

LONDON – WEST

Charing Cross Hospital – Macmillan
 Support Team
Great Ormond Street Hospital for Sick
 Children – Symptom Care Team
London Lighthouse
The Middlesex Hospital – Cancer
 Counsellors
Paddington Community Hospital –
 Pembridge Continuing Care Unit
The Royal National Throat, Nose & Ear
 Hospital – Cancer Counsellor
University College Hospital – Macmillan
 Service

GREATER MANCHESTER

Beswick – Beswick Health Centre –
 Macmillan Service
Manchester – Hulme Combined Clinic –
 Macmillan Service
Oldham – Dr Kershaw's Hospice
 St Peter's House – Macmillan Service
Radcliffe – Hospice for Bury
 Association
Rochdale – Community Services Unit –
 Macmillan Service
 Springhill Hospice
Stockport – Stockport Terminal Care
 Team
Urmston – Macmillan Service
Withington – Christie Hospital –
 Macmillan Hospital Support Nurse
Worsley – St Ann's Hospice

MERSEYSIDE

Liverpool – Broadgreen Hospital –
 Macmillan Service
 Fazakerley Hospital – Continuing
 Care Service
 Royal Liverpool Hospital – Macmillan
 Service
 St Joseph's Hospice Association –
 Hospice International
 Sefton General Hospital – Macmillan
 Service
 Sunnybank Marie Curie Home

Southport – Macmillan Service
 Southport General Infirmary –
 Queenscourt
St Helen's – Fairfield House, Fairfield
 Hospital
 St Helen's Hospital – Macmillan
 Service
Wirral – Arrowe Park Hospital –
 Macmillan Service
 Bebington Health Clinic – Macmillan
 Service
 Pensby Clinic – Macmillan Service
 St John's Hospice in Wirral

MIDDLESEX

Ashford – Ashford Hospital –
 Macmillan Service
Harrow – Harrow Hospital –
 Continuing Care Team
Hayes – Victoria Lodge
Isleworth – West Middlesex University
 Hospital – Clinical Nurse Specialist
Northwood – Mount Vernon Hospital –
 Michael Sobell House
Southall – Ealing Hospital – Meadow
 House
Wembley – St Luke's Hospice

NORFOLK

Great Yarmouth – James Paget Hospital
 – Macmillan Service
Holt – Kelling Hospital – Macmillan
 Service
King's Lynn – Queen Elizabeth Hospital
 – Macmillan Service
 West Norfolk Home Hospice Support
Norwich – Priscilla Bacon Lodge

NORTHAMPTONSHIRE

Daventry – Daventry Health Centre –
 Macmillan Service
Kettering – Stockburn Memorial Home
 – Macmillan Service
Northampton – Cynthia Spencer House

NOTTINGHAMSHIRE

Mansfield – Oak Tree Lane Health
 Centre – Macmillan Service
Nottingham – City Hospital – Hayward
 House
 The Nottinghamshire Hospice
Sutton-in-Ashfield – King's Mill Hospice
 Trust
Worksop – Bassetlaw Hospice of the
 Good Shepherd Appeal

Larwood Health Centre – Macmillan Service

OXFORDSHIRE

Banbury – Katharine House Hospice
Orchard Health Centre – Macmillan Service
Henley-on-Thames – Sue Ryder Home, Nettlebed
Oxford – The Churchill Hospital – Sir Michael Sobell House
Helen House

SHROPSHIRE

Bridgnorth – Bridgnorth Child Health Centre – Macmillan Service
Shrewsbury – Royal Shrewsbury Hospital (South) – Macmillan Service
Shropshire & Mid Wales Hospice
Telford – Macmillan Home Care Team

SOMERSET

Taunton – St Margaret's Somerset Hospice
Musgrove Park Hospital – Symptom Control Team

STAFFORDSHIRE

Lichfield – St Giles Hospice
Stafford – Hospice at Home
Stoke-on-Trent – The Douglas Macmillan Home
Stone – Trent Hospital – Macmillan Service

SUFFOLK

Bury St Edmunds – St Nicholas's Hospice
Ipswich – Allington Clinic – Macmillan Service
St Elizabeth Hospice

SURREY

Camberley – Ridgewood Centre – Macmillan Service
Caterham – Harestone Marie Curie Home
Cheam – St Raphael's Hospice
Chertsey – St Peter's Hospital – Macmillan Nurse
Dorking – Hospice Home Care Surrey
Esher – The Princess Alice Hospice

Farnham – Phyllis Tuckwell Memorial Hospice
Godalming – Milford Hospital – Macmillan Service
Guildford – Royal Surrey County Hospital – Macmillan Hospital Support Nurse
Kingston – Kingston Hospital – Macmillan Continuing Care Team
Leatherhead – Rainbow Trust
Redhill – East Surrey Hospital – Macmillan Service
Reigate – The East Surrey Health Authority Symptom Control Team
Sutton – Royal Marsden Hospital – Continuing Care Unit
Weybridge – Weybridge Hospital – Sam Beare Continuing Care Service

SUSSEX

Brighton – Community Hospice Team Copper Cliff
Royal Sussex County Hospital – Macmillan Service (Breast Care Nurse)
The Tarner Home
Chichester – St Wilfrid's Hospice
Crawley – St Catherine's Hospice
Eastbourne – Princess Alice Hospital – Macmillan Service
St Wilfrid's Hospice (Eastbourne)
Hastings – Hastings Health Authority – Macmillan Service
Midhurst – West Sussex Macmillan Service
St Leonards-on-Sea – St Michael's Hospice (Hastings)
Wivelsfield Green – St Peter's and St James's
Worthing – St Barnabas's Hospice

TYNE & WEAR

Gateshead – Gateshead Health Centre – Macmillan Service
Hebburn – Hebburn Health Centre – Macmillan Service
Jarrow – Monkton Hall Hospital – South Tyneside Special Care Team
Newcastle upon Tyne – Conrad House Marie Curie Home
Newcastle General Hospital – Macmillan Nurse Support Team
St Oswald's Hospice
South Shields – St Clare's Hospice
Sunderland – St Benedict's Hospice

WARWICKSHIRE

Coventry – Stoke Aldermoor Clinic –
    Macmillan Service
Leamington Spa – Crown Way Clinic –
    Macmillan Service
Nuneaton – George Eliot Hospital –
    Macmillan Service
  George Eliot Hospital – Mary Ann
    Evans Unit
Warwick – Myton Hamlet Hospice
  Myton Hamlet Hospice – Macmillan
    Service
  South Warwickshire Hospital –
    Macmillan Service

WEST MIDLANDS

Birmingham – Acorns – The Children's
    Hospice Trust
  Dudley Road Hospital – Macmillan
    Service
  Hall Green Clinic – Macmillan Service
  St Mary's Hospice
  Taylor Memorial Home
Brierley Hill – Brierley Hill Health
    Centre – Dudley Oncology/
    Macmillan Team
Solihull – Marston Green Hospital –
    Solihull Macmillan Service
  Warren Pearl Marie Curie Home
Walsall – Leckie House – Macmillan
    Service
  Manor Hospital – Macmillan Service
Wolverhampton – Compton Hall
    Hospice

WILTSHIRE

Salisbury – Odstock Hospital –
    Salisbury Macmillan Unit
Swindon – Prospect Foundation

WORCESTERSHIRE

Bromsgrove – Primrose Hospice
Kidderminster – Kidderminster General
    Hospital – Terminal Care Support
    Group
Stourport – Stourport Health Centre –
    Macmillan Service
Worcester – St Richard's Hospice
    Foundation

YORKSHIRE – NORTH

Harrogate – Harrogate General Hospital
    – Macmillan Service
  St Michael's Hospice

Scarborough – St Catherine's Hospice
York – The Health Centre – Macmillan
    Service
  St Leonard's Hospice

YORKSHIRE – SOUTH

Doncaster – Doncaster Hospice Appeal
  Doncaster Royal Infirmary –
    Symptom Control Team
Rotherham – Doncaster Gate Hospital
    – Macmillan Service
  Rotherham Hospice Trust
Sheffield – Northern General Hospital –
    Macmillan Service
  Royal Hallamshire Hospital –
    Macmillan Support Nurses
  St Luke's Hospice

YORKSHIRE – WEST

Bradford – Edmund Street Clinic –
    Macmillan Service
Halifax – Overgate Hospice
  Royal Halifax Infirmary – Macmillan
    Service
Huddersfield – Kirkwood Hospice
Ilkley – Ardenlea Marie Curie Home
Keighley – Sue Ryder Home
Leeds – Kirkstall Clinic – Macmillan
    Service
  St Gemma's Hospice
  St James University Hospital –
    Macmillan Service
  Seacroft and Killingbeck Hospitals –
    Macmillan Service
  Wheatfields Hospice
Pontefract – Five Towns Plus Hospice
    Fund
Wakefield – Pinderfields General
    Hospital – Wakefield Hospital
    Support Team
  Wakefield Hospice
Wetherby – Martin House

SCOTLAND

BORDERS

Melrose – Borders General Hospital –
    Macmillan Palliative Care Service

CENTRAL

Denny – Strathcarron Hospice

DUMFRIES & GALLOWAY

Dumfries – Dumfries and Galloway
  Royal Infirmary – Alexandra Unit

FIFE

Kirkcaldy – Kirkcaldy Health Centre –
  Macmillan Service

GRAMPIAN

Aberdeen – Tor-na-Dee Hospital –
  Roxburghe House
Elgin – Health Centre – Grampian West
  Macmillan Service

HIGHLAND

Inverness – Highland Hospice
  Raigmore Hospital – Macmillan
  Service

LOTHIAN

Broxburn – Sue Ryder Home
Edinburgh – Fairmile Marie Curie
  Home
  Milestone Venture Trust
  St Columba's Hospice
Livingston – Dedridge Health Centre –
  West Lothian Macmillan Service

STRATHCLYDE

Airdrie – St Andrew's Hospice
Ayr – The Ayrshire Hospice
Clydebank – St Margaret's Hospice
Glasgow – Belvedere Hospital –
  Macmillan Service
  Hunters Hill Marie Curie Home
  Prince & Princess of Wales Hospice
  Victoria Infirmary – Macmillan
  Hospital Support Team
Greenock – Ardgowan Hospice
Johnstone – St Vincent's Hospice
Kilmarnock – Crosshouse Hospital –
  Continuing Care Unit
Newmains – Newmains Health Centre –
  Macmillan Service
Paisley – Accord Hospice
Port Glasgow – Port Glasgow Health
  Centre – Macmillan Service

TAYSIDE

Dundee – Royal Victoria Hospital –
  Roxburghe House
Perth – Macmillan House

WALES

CLWYD

Denbigh – Denbighshire Infirmary –
  Macmillan Service
Holywell – Greenfields Clinic –
  Macmillan Service
Old Colwyn – Colwyn Bay Community
  Hospital – Macmillan Service
Prestatyn – Prestatyn Community
  Hospital – Macmillan Service
  St Kentigern Hospice
Wrexham – Wrexham Maelor Hospital
  – Nightingale House

DYFED

Aberystwyth – Bronglais General
  Hospital – Macmillan Service
Ammanford – Amman Valley Hospital
Carmarthen – West Wales General
  Hospital – Macmillan Service
Haverfordwest – Meyler House –
  Macmillan Service
  The Paul Sartori Foundation
Pembroke Dock – South Pembrokeshire
  Hospital
Tenby – Tenby Cottage Hospital –
  Macmillan Service

GLAMORGAN

Bridgend – Y-Bwthyn Day Centre
Cardiff – George Thomas Centre for
  Hospice Care
Merthyr Tydfil – The Hollies Health
  Centre – Macmillan Service
  St Tydfil's Hospital – Macmillan
  Service
Mountain Ash – Mountain Ash General
  Hospital – Macmillan Service
Penarth – Holme Tower Marie Curie
  Home
Pontypridd – Pontypridd & District
  Hospital – Macmillan Service
Rhondda – Treherbert Hospital
Swansea – Morriston Hospital –
  Ty-Olwen

GWENT

Blackwood – Oakdale Hospital
Monmouth – Monmouth General
  Hospital
Newport – St David's Foundation

GWYNEDD

Caernarfon – Brynseiont Hospital –
Macmillan Service
Llandudno – St David's Hospice
Foundation – Aberconwy Appeal

NORTHERN IRELAND

Ballinmallard – Fermanagh Support
Group
Ballymena – Cottage Hospital –
Macmillan Service
Belfast – Beaconfield Marie Curie Home
Northern Ireland Hospice
Coleraine – Macmillan Homecare
Service
Derry – Foyle Hospice

REPUBLIC OF IRELAND

Blackrock – St Francis Hospice
Castletroy – Little Company of Mary
Hospice
Cork – Marymount Hospice
Dublin – Our Lady's Hospice
Galway – Galway Hospice Service
Kilkenny – St Luke's Hospital – Carlow/
Kilkenny Home Care Team
Letterkenny – Foyle Hospice – Donegal
Branch

CHANNEL ISLANDS

Grouville – Jersey Hospice Care
St Peter Port – Lukis House – Hospice
Care Sisters

ISLE OF MAN

Douglas – St Bridget's Hospice

Town and City List

ABBREVIATIONS

AIDS – willing to accept suitable AIDS
patients

C.AIDS – considering possibility of taking
suitable AIDS patients

B – number of beds

BS – bereavement service

DC – day-care facilities

HC – home-care service (hospices without
their own home-care service are often in
close touch with local home-care teams)

HST – hospital support team

MD – medical director in team

MiniMac – small wards (usually 2 beds
with visitor's room), attached to
community hospitals in Wales; built and
equipped by Cancer Relief and run by
NHS

MND/OTI – willing to accept suitable
patients with motor-neurone disease
and/or other terminal illnesses

MS – willing, in particular, to take patients
with multiple sclerosis

NS – number of nursing staff

OT/PT – occupational therapy and/or
physiotherapy provided

T – training provided (wide variation in
type and extent of courses)

WTE – whole-time equivalent

ABERDEEN, GRAMPIAN

Roxburghe House
Tor-na-Dee Hospital
Milltimber
Aberdeen
AB1 0HR
Tel. 0224 681818, ext 55641

Location: Outskirts of Aberdeen on A93
Catchment: Grampian area (& Shetland/
Orkney)
Contacts: Medical Director – Dr John
Berkeley
Sister – Mrs Margaret Bellamy
Secretary – Mrs Anne Clements

B – 21, BS, MND/OTI, MD, NS – 24 WTE

★ A day unit with 10 places will be
opening in 1990.

ABERYSTWYTH, DYFED

Macmillan Service
Ceredigion Health Unit
Bronglais General Hospital
Aberystwyth
Tel. 0970 623131

Contact: Director of Nursing Services
– Mr P. Johnson

HC, DC

★ Ceredigion Health Management also
considering in-patient beds.

AIRDRIE, STRATHCLYDE

St Andrew's Hospice
Henderson Street
Airdrie
ML6 6AS
Tel. 0236 66951

Location: ½ mile north-east of town
centre (north side of A89)
Catchment: Lanarkshire
Contacts: Matron – Sister Catherine
Egan
Consultant – Dr C.J. Sugden

B – 10, BS, T, C. AIDS, MND/OTI, NS – 35

★ There are also 20 beds for long-stay
geriatric patients.

ANMMANFORD, DYFED

Amman Valley Hospital
Folland Road
Glanamman
Ammanford
Tel. 0269 822226

MiniMac – 2 beds.

ANDOVER, HAMPSHIRE

Countess of Brecknock House
*Andover War Memorial Community
Hospital*
Charlton Road
Andover
SP10 3LB
Tel. 0264 58811

Location: Within ½ mile of rail station in
Charlton direction (north-west of
Andover)
Catchment: Winchester Health
Authority, north of Countess
Mountbatten House catchment
area
Contact: Hospital and sector Manager –
Mrs M. Antrobus

B – 6, HC, DC, OT/PT, BS, AIDS, MD

★ This is a *project*, due to open in March
1990.

ASHBY-DE-LA-ZOUCH,
LEICESTERSHIRE

Sue Ryder Home for Continuing Care
Staunton Harold Hall
Ashby-de-la-Zouch
LE6 5RT
Tel. 0332 862798

Catchment: West Leicestershire, South
Derbyshire, Nottinghamshire and
Staffordshire
Contact: Matron – Mrs Margaret
Bostock

B – 10, MND/OTI

★ Opened April 1989. Beds to increase
to 29 later on and other services will be
added.

ASHFORD, MIDDLESEX

Macmillan Service
Dymott House
Ashford Hospital
London Road
Ashford
Tel. 0784 251188, ext 4110

HC, AIDS

ASHTON UNDER LYNE,
LANCASHIRE

Macmillan Service
Tameside General Hospital
Ashton under Lyne
OL6 9RW
Tel. 061 330 8373, ext 6453

AYLESBURY,
BUCKINGHAMSHIRE

Aylesbury Vale Hospice Project
The Old Diabetic Unit
Stoke Mandeville Hospital
Mandeville Road
Aylesbury
HP21 8AL
Tel. 0296 29975

Contacts: Appeal Director – Mrs
Barbara Lucas
Medical Director – Dr S.J. Williams
Macmillan home care already in
operation

★ Building with 10-bed unit due to open
autumn 1989.

AYR, STRATHCLYDE

The Ayrshire Hospice
35 Racecourse Road
Ayr
KA7 2TG
Tel. 0292 269200

Location: ½ mile from town centre,
south on A719
Catchment: Ayrshire & Arran Health
Board

Contacts: Administrator – Mrs Helen W.
Blythe
Matron – Mrs Dora E. Storey
Medical Director – Dr John C. Bass
Home-care contact: home-care nurse –
0292 269200

B – 11, HC, DC, BS, T, MD, NS – 14 WTE

★ Beds to increase to 15 in January 1990.

BAKEWELL, DERBYSHIRE

Macmillan Service
The Cottage Hospital
Bakewell
DE4 1EB
Tel. 0629 812680

Location: first turning on left off B5055
(Monyash Road)
Catchment: North Derbyshire
Contacts: Macmillan sisters – Jean
Fenely, Maureen Cohen

HC, BS, AIDS, NS – 2

★ There are plans for a future day
hospice to be based in Chapel en le Frith.

BALLINMALLARD, CO.
FERMANAGH

Fernmanagh Support Group
Mullaghmeen House
Ballinmallard
Tel. 0365 81555

Contacts: Lady Anthony Hamilton
Co-ordinator – Director of Nursing
services – Mrs Egan

★ Planning day care; already funding
nurse training and equipment purchase.

BALLYMENA, CO. ANTRIM

Macmillan Service
Cottage Hospital
Duke Street
Ballymena
Tel. 0332 781836

BANBURY, OXFORDSHIRE

Katharine House Hospice
c/o Crest Hotels
Bridge Street
Banbury
LX16 8RQ
Tel. 0295 62100

Contacts: Margaret Kelly
Neil Gadsby

Home-care contact: Mrs Jill Tewson –
0295 59851

HC, BS, T

★ Day care is due to start in autumn 1990
and in-patient beds will be opened as
soon as possible thereafter.

Macmillan Service
Orchard Health Centre
Cope Road
Banbury
OX16 7EZ
Tel. 0295 59851

Location: ⅓ mile north-north-west from
Banbury Cross
Catchment: North Oxfordshire
Contact: Macmillan nurses

HC, BS, AIDS, NS – 2

BARNET, HERTFORDSHIRE

Barnet Support Team
Barnet General Hospital
Wellhouse Lane
Barnet
EN5 3DJ
Tel. 01 440 5111, ext 4446

Location: A1000 to top of Barnet hill,
fork left (large church in centre of
road) into Wood Street, fifth turning
on left.
Catchment: eastern half of Barnet & parts
of South-West Hertfordshire Health
Authority
Contact: Senior Nurse – Miss Janet H.
Doyle

HST, BS, T, AIDS, MND/OTI, NS – 4

BARNSTAPLE, DEVON

Hospice Care Trust – North Devon
7 New Buildings
Vicarage Street
Barnstaple
EX32 8BL
Tel. 0271 44248

Location: town centre opposite the
health centre
Catchment: North Devon District
Council & Torridge District Council
Contact: Administrator – Philip Jewell
Senior Nurse – Anne Belchamber
Home-care contact: Anne Belchamber

HC, DC, BS, AIDS,* MND, NS – 5

* Planning to accept AIDS patients if they have a
concomitant cancer.

BARROW IN FURNESS, CUMBRIA

Macmillan Service
Fairfield Clinic
2 Fairfield Lane
Barrow in Furness
Tel. 0229 20552

HC

BARTESTREE, HEREFORD

St Michael's Hospice
Bartestree
Hereford
HR1 4HA
Tel. 0432 851000

Location: 4 miles east of Hereford city on A438, behind Bartestree convent
Catchment: For in-patient care, no exclusions but mainly from Herefordshire, south Worcestershire & parts of Gloucestershire, Shropshire & Powys.
For home-care patients – Herefordshire
Contacts: Medical Director – Dr T. Keeble
Adminstrative secretary – Mrs A. Mountford

B – 16, HC, DC, OT/PT, BS, T, AIDS, MND/OTI, MD, NS – 22

BASILDON, ESSEX

Macmillan Nurses
Nurses' Campus
Level 6
Basildon Hospital
Basildon
SS16 5NL
Tel. 0268 3911, ext 3855/3624

Catchment: Basildon & Thurrock Health Authority
Contact: Macmillan nurses

HC, BS, T, AIDS, NS – 2

St Luke's Hospice
Fobbing Farm
Nethermayne
Basildon
SS16 5NJ
Tel. 0268 24973

Location: ¾ mile from Basildon town centre on A176, adjacent to Basildon Hospital
Catchment: Basildon & Thurrock Health Authority

Contact: Matron – Mrs Trudy Cox
Home-care contact: Basildon Hospital – 0268 3911

BS, T

★ At present bereavement support and a sitting service are provided. Day care is planned for spring 1990 and an in-patient unit for autumn 1990.

BASINGSTOKE, HAMPSHIRE

Macmillan Service
Basingstoke & District Hospital
Aldermaston Road
Basingstoke
RG24 9NA
Tel. 0256 473202

Catchment: Referrals from hospital & community within Basingstoke & North Hampshire Health District

HST, MND, AIDS, T

BATH, AVON

The Dorothy House Foundation
Macmillan House
164 Bloomfield Road
Bath
BA2 2AT
Tel. 0225 311335/318368/445545

Location: 1 mile from city centre, branch of A367 (Radstock Road into Bloomfield Road)
Catchment: Bath District Health Authority
Contacts: General Manager – Mr T.F. Mears
Senior Nurse/Patient Care Services – Mrs B. Bevan
Home-care contact: Mrs Barbara Bevan – 0225 311335/318368/445545

B – 6, HC, DC, OT/PT, BS, T, C.AIDS, MND/OTI, NS – 10.1

BEACONSFIELD, BUCKINGHAMSHIRE

The Iain Rennie Hospice at Home
63 Burkes Road
Beaconsfield
HP9 1PW
Tel. 0494 678529/0296 630368

Location: ½ mile from Beaconsfield new town (office only)

Catchment: Chiltern area of South
    Buckinghamshire & Hertfordshire
Contacts: Chairman, Council of
    Management – Mr Eric Robson
Senior Nursing Sister – Mrs Mary
    Robson
Senior Nursing Sister – Mrs Daphne
    Vessey

HC, BS, C, AIDS, MND/OTI, NS – 18

*The South Bucks Hospice – Universal
    Hospice Trust*
Appeals Office
25 Waller Road
Beaconsfield
HP9 2HD
Tel. 0494 676831 (evenings)

Location: not yet known
Contacts: Secretary – Edie Pusey
    Chairman – Tony Hardware

★ This is a *project*, planned to open in
1991, which will offer day care for 20
patients as well as 2 or 3 respite beds.

**BELFAST, NORTHERN
IRELAND**

Beaconsfield Marie Curie Home
Kensington Road
Belfast
BT5 6NF
Tel. 0232 794200

Location: based at Knock near the
    intersection of the ring road with
    Upper Newtownards Road
Contact: Matron/Manager – Mrs M.J.
    Harper

B – 20, BS, T, AIDS*, MD, NS – 27

* AIDS patients accepted if they have cancer.

★ Number of beds to increase to 29
mid-1990.

Northern Ireland Hospice
74 Somerton Road
Belfast
BT15 3LH
Tel. 0232 781836

Location: 1½ miles north of Belfast city
    centre
Catchment: Northern Ireland
Contacts: Adminstrative Director –
    Peter S. Quigley
Medical Director – Dr Yvonne Duff
Nursing Director – Mrs Rita Beattie

Home-care contact: Miss Liz McKee –
    0232 781836

B – 15, HC, DC, OT/PT, BS, T, AIDS, MND/OTI,
MD, NS – 21. 6 WTE + 'bank' nurses

★ An extension is planned to increase the
number of beds to 25 in 1990.

**BERKHAMSTED,
HERTFORDSHIRE**

*The Hospice of St Francis
    (Berkhamsted) Limited*
27 Shrublands Road
Berkhamsted
Herts
HP4 3HX
Tel. 0442 862960/0442 873048

Location: Residential location – parallel
    to A41
Catchment: North West Hertfordshire,
    South West Hertfordshire,
    Wycombe District, Aylesbury Vale
    District
Contacts: Medical Director – Dr H.M.
    O'Conor
Administrator – Mrs L. Craven
Matron – Mrs H.N. McNair
Home Care Contact: Matron – Mrs H.N.
    McNair – 0442 862960/873048

B – 8, HC, DC, OT/PT, BS, T, AIDS, MND/OTI,
MD, NS – 16

BESWICK, MANCHESTER

Macmillan Service
Beswick Health Centre
Ranworth Close
Beswick
M11 3SL
Tel. 061 223 6385

Location: off Graymore Lane (A6010)
Catchment: North Manchester Health
    District
Contacts: Macmillan nurses – Jane
    Abbott, Anne Kehoe

HC, BS, AIDS, NS – 2

**BIRMINGHAM, WEST
MIDLANDS**

Acorns – The Children's Hospice Trust
103 Oak Tree Lane
Selly Oak
Birmingham
B29 5HZ
Tel. 021 414 1741

Location: 4 miles south-west of city
    centre

Catchment: West Midlands Regional
    Health Authority
Contact: Hospice Director – Miss Sally
    Day
Home-care contact: 021 414 1789

B – 10, HC, BS, AIDS, MND/OTI, NS – 13 WTE

★ Acorns offers home support, respite
and terminal care to children with a
limited life expectancy

Macmillan Service
Dudley Road Hospital
Ward S4
Winson Green
Birmingham
B18 7QH
Tel. 021 554 3801/200 1616

Referrals from hospital only.

Macmillan Service
Hall Green Clinic
5 Green Road
Hall Green
Birmingham
B28
Tel. 021 778 3734

HC

St Mary's Hospice
176 Raddlebarn Road
Selly Park
Birmingham
B29 7DA
Tel. 021 472 1191

Location: 2½ miles south-west of city
    centre, just off A38
Catchment: Greater Birmingham
Contacts: Medical Director – Dr W.D.
    Rees
Matron – Mrs S. ten Cate-Oxby
Director of Education – Miss J.M.
    Ellis
Adminstrative Director – Mr D.T.
    Johnson
Home-care contact: Home-Care Team
    Leader – 021 472 1191

B – 25, HC, DC, BS, T, AIDS, MND/OTI, MD, NS –
43.5 WTE

Taylor Memorial Home
76 Grange Road
Erdington
Birmningham 24
Tel. 021 373 5526

Contacts: Acting Medical Director – Dr
    S. Perkins

Nursing Officer – Mrs E. Parsons
Administrator – Mr S. Arnold
Social Worker – Mr P. Tobin

B – 32, HC, DC, BS, T

BLACKBURN, LANCASHIRE

East Lancashire Hospice
Park Lee Road
Blackburn
BB2 3NY
Tel. 0254 54064

Catchment: Blackburn, Hyndburn &
    Ribble Valley
Contacts: Consultant – Dr M. Seigleman
Senior Sister – E. Roberts
Home-care contact: Sister M. Marshall –
    0254 54064

B – 10, HC, DC, OT/PT, BS, T, AIDS, MD, NS – 11
WTE

BLACKPOOL, LANCASHIRE

Trinity – the Hospice in the Fylde
Low Moor Road
Bispham
Blackpool
FY2 OBG
Tel. 0253 58881

Location: 1½ miles north-west of town
    centre, 4 miles from the end of the
    M55
Contacts: Medical Director – Dr J.D.
    Cooper
Matron – Mrs B. Head
Bursar – Mr F.J. Baron

B – 30, HC, OT/PT, BS, T, AIDS,* MND/OTI, MD,
NS – 42

* Willing to accept AIDS patients for home care if
requested. AIDS in-patients treated at District General
Hospital until terminal stages.

★ Planning to open a day hospice.

Macmillan Service
Victoria Hospital
Whinney Heys Road
Blackpool
FY3 8NR
Tel. 0253 34111

BLACKROCK, CO. DUBLIN

St Francis Hospice
Station Road
Raheny
Dublin 5

Tel. 0001 327535 (9am–5pm,
weekdays), 901884, unit 9229
(evenings and weekends)

HC

BLACKWOOD, GWENT

Oakdale Hospital
Blackwood
NP2 OJH
Tel. 0495 225207

MiniMac – 2 beds

BOLTON, LANCASHIRE

a) *Bolton Hospice*
c/o Mr W.B. Kirwin (Nurse Adviser)
144 Markland Hill Lane
Bolton
BL1 5NZ
Tel. 0204 40316

b) *Bolton Hospice*
Campaign Site Office
Queens Park Street
Bolton
BL1 4QT
Tel. 0204 364375

B – 14, HC, DC, OT/PT, BS, T, C, AIDS, MND/OTI

★ This is a *project* which hopes to open in
1990, although home care may be
available earlier.

Macmillan Service
Hulton Hospital
Hulton Lane
Bolton
BL3 4JZ
Tel. 0204 390272

HC

BOSTON, LINCOLNSHIRE

Macmillan Nursing Service
Boston Health Clinic
Lincoln Lane
Boston
PE21 8RT
Tel. 0205 60880

Location: in town centre
Catchment: South Lincolnshire Health
Authority
Contacts: Glenys Crawley – 0205 60880
Cathy Jones – 0476 590805

HC, BS, T, AIDS, NS – 2

BOURNEMOUTH, DORSET

Poole Hospice Project
c/o Westover Chambers
Hinton Road
Bournemouth
BH1 2EQ
Tel. 0202 23663 (administration only)

Location: 2 miles from Poole Town
Centre, 1½ miles from West
Bournemouth
Catchment: Poole, Purbecks, West
Bournemouth & surrounding areas
Contact: Chairman of the Lewis-Manning
Cancer Trust – Mr A.C. Roberts

★ This is a recently set up *project* which
hopes to provide in-patient beds, home
care, day care and staff training by
1990–91.

BRADFORD, WEST YORKSHIRE

Macmillan Service
Edmund East Clinic
26 Edmund Street
Bradford
BD5 OBH
Tel. 0274 728421

Location: in town centre, between
Morley Street & Little Horton Lane
Catchment: Bradford Health Authority
area only – this does *not* cover all
the Bradford metropolitan area
Contact: Locality Manager – Mrs P.
Cooper
Home-care contact: Macmillan nurses –
0274 728421

HC, BS, AIDS, MND/OTI

BRIDGEND, GLAMORGAN

Y-Bwthyn Day Centre
Y Bwthyn
Nolten Street
Bridgend
Tel. 0656 68030

Location: town centre, the foot of Court
Road which leads to the station
Catchment: Oqwr – radius 25 miles
Contacts: Volunteer Co-ordinator – Mr
Geoffrey Foster
Director of Nursing – Miss Burns,
Princess of Wales Hospital,
Bridgend
Medical Director – Dr Pam Powell
Home-care contact: Home Care Sisters –
0656 68030

Community Sister – 0656 645019

HC, DC, OT, BS – 2 back-up beds

BRIDGNORTH, SHROPSHIRE

Macmillan Service
Bridgnorth Child Health Centre
Northgate
Bridgnorth
WV16 4ET
Tel. 07462 3357

BRIERLEY HILL, WEST MIDLANDS

Dudley Oncology/Macmillan Team
Brierley Hill Health Centre
Albion Street
Brierley Hill
DY5 3EE
Tel. 0384 480088

Location: town centre
Catchment: Metropolitan Borough of Dudley
Contact: Senior Nurse – Chris Stanley

HC, BS, NS – 3

BRIGHTON, EAST SUSSEX

Community Hospice Team – Brighton
4 Tilbury Place
Brighton
BN2 2GY
Tel. 0273 604331

Location: near town centre (office only)
Catchment: Brighton Health Authority
Contacts: Dr Jean Kay
  Senior Nursing Sister – Sister Gena Lambert
Home-care contact: Maggi Langley (Adminstrator) 0273 604331

HC, BS, T, AIDS, MND/OTI, MD, NS – 4 F/T &p/t

Copper Cliff
74 Redhill Drive
Brighton
BN1 5FL
Tel. 0273 504842

Location: 2 miles north of town centre – near A23
Catchment: Brighton, Hove, Lewes, Peacehaven, Newhaven
Contacts: Chairman of Management Committee – Mr R.H. Braybon
  Matron – Miss J.J. James

B – 18, NS – 30

Macmillan Service
Department of Breast and Stoma Care
c/o Latilla Department
Royal Sussex County Hospital
Eastern Road
Brighton
BN2 5BE
Tel. 0273 606126

Breast-care nurse.

The Tarner Home
1 Tilbury Place
Brighton
BN2 2GY
Tel. 0273 604665

Location: town centre
Catchment: East Brighton
Contact: Secretary – Mr D.M. Arnold

B – 14, OT/PT, BS, MND/OTI, MD, NS – 12

BRISTOL, AVON

St Peter's Hospice
St Agnes Avenue
Knowle
Bristol
BS4 2DU
Tel. 0272 774605

Location: 3 miles south from town centre, just off the A37
Catchment: the whole of Avon approx.
Contacts: Administrator – Mr M. Coe
  Medical Director – Dr I. Capstick
  Nursing Director – Mrs H. Salway

B – 14, HC, DC, BS, T, MD, NS –30

BROADSTAIRS, KENT

Macmillan Nursing Service
Broadstairs Health Centre
The Broadway
Broadstairs
CT10 2AJ
Tel. 0843 602654

Catchment: Thanet
Contact: Macmillan nurse

HC, BS

BROMSGROVE, WORCESTERSHIRE

Primrose Hospice Ltd
Fox Lane
Bromsgrove
B61 7EG
Tel. 0527 71051

Location: 1 mile south-west of town
centre on Hilltop Hospital site
Catchment: Bromsgrove & Redditch
Contacts: Appeals Director/
Administrator –Miss Nichola G.
Hackett
Senior Sister – Miss Jean Lucas

HC. DC. OT/PT. BS. T. NS –1.8

BROXBURN, LOTHIAN

Sue Ryder Home
Binny House
Ecclesmachan Road
Uphall
Broxburn
EH52 6NL
Tel. 0506 856023

Contact: Matron – Mrs J.M. Morris

B – 6 (+ 17 beds for MND/MS)

BUDLEIGH SALTERTON, DEVON

Budleigh Salterton & District
Hospiscare
The Health Centre
1 The Lawn
Budleigh Salterton
EX9 6LS
Tel. 03954 3629/2213

Location: town centre
Catchment: Budleigh Salterton &
parishes of East Budleigh, Otterton,
Colaton Raleigh, Woodbury
Contacts: Chairman – Dr Graham
Taylor
Secretary – Peter Walsh
Treasurer – Raymond Newcombe
Home-care contact: Mrs Hanneke Coates
– 03954 2310

HC. BS. T. AIDS*. MND. OTI. NS – 1

* Patients with AIDS. MND and other terminal illness
can be helped by the volunteer home help service but
not by the Macmillan nurse.

BURNLEY, LANCASHIRE

Macmillan Service
Community Sector Offices
Burnley General Hospital
Casterton Avenue
Burnley
BB10 2PQ
Tel. 0282 25071, ext 2484

Location: 2 miles north of Burnley
centre, on A6114

Catchment: Burnley, Pendle &
Rossendale
Contact: Acting Director Nursing
Services (Community) – Miss M.
Malley
Home-care contacts: Macmillan nurses –
Mrs Kay Humphreys, Mrs Carole
Bridge – 0282 25071, ext 2484
(9–10 am and 4–5 pm)

HC. BS. T. AIDS.* NS – 2

* AIDS patients accepted if they have cancer.

The Secretary
Hospice Care for Burnley & Pendle
Newfield House
Higher Red Lees
Cliviger
Burnley

Home-care contact: Volunteers
Co-ordinator – 0282 33740

HC

★ Home care provided by volunteers in
conjunction with local Macmillan nurses.
Plans for a day-care unit in late 1989/early
1990.

BURY, LANCASHIRE

Macmillan Service
The Community Nursing Officer
Parsons Lane
Bury
BL9 0JZ
Tel. 061 764 2422

HC

★ Estimated opening date is spring 1990.

A Hospice for Bury Association
Bealey Community Hospital
Dumors Lane
Radcliffe
Bury
Tel. not yet known

Location: 1 mile from Radcliffe town
centre, 1 mile from A56
Catchment: predominantly the area of
Bury Borough
Contact: Chairman of Bury Hospice
Association – Mr C.A. Caffrey,
39 Watling Street, Bury BL8 2JD

★ This is a *project* which plans to open a
5-bed hospice with day care – estimated
opening date is March 1990.

BURY ST EDMUNDS, SUFFOLK

St Nicholas' Hospice
Turret Close
24 Westgate Street
Bury St Edmunds
IP33 1QC
Tel. 0284 754446 (medical); 766133
(administration)

Catchment: West Suffolk Health
Authority
Contact: Director of Nursing/
Adminstrator – Mrs R.M. Clare
Home-care contact: Mrs June Storey –
. 0284 754446

HC, DC, OT/PT, BS, AIDS, MND/OTI, MD, NS – 4
WTE

CAERNARFON, GWYNEDD

Macmillan Service
Brynseiont Hospital
Caernarfon
LL55 2YO
Tel. 0286 2900, ext 29; 3371/2809

MiniMac (4 beds) + HC

CAMBERLEY, SURREY

Macmillan Service
Ridgewood Centre
Old Bisley Road
Frimley
Camberley
GU16 5QT
Tel. 0276 21675

Location: 2 miles from Frimley Park
Hospital, Portsmouth Road, Frimley
Catchment: West Surrey, North-East
Hampshire Health Authority
(Aldershot, Ash, Farnham, Fleet,
Yately, Farnborough & Surrey
Heath)
Contacts: Director of Nursing Services
(Community) – Mr R. Addison
Community Nurse Manager (District
Nursing) – Mrs M. Blackman
both at Community Nursing Office, 11
Church Road, Frimley, Surrey
Macmillan nurses – 0276 21675
(answerphone)

HC, BS, T, NS – 2

CAMBRIDGE, CAMBRIDGESHIRE

Arthur Rank House
Macmillan Continuing Care Unit

Brookfields Hospital
351 Mill Road
Cambridge
CB1 3DF
Tel. 0223 245926

Contacts: Medical Director – Dr Tim
Hunt
Senior Nurse – Sister Mary Brown

B – 24, HC

CANTERBURY, KENT

Pilgrims Hospice
56 London Road
Canterbury
CT2 8JY
Tel. 0227 459700/457766

Location: 1 mile north of town centre,
near the 'ring road'
Catchment: the NHS Health Districts of
Canterbury & Thanet & south-east
Kent
Contacts: Bursar – Colonel P.G.
Thompson
Medical Director – Dr S.R. Kirkham
Matron – Mrs A. Campbell
Home-care contact: The secretaries –
0227 459700/457766

B – 20, HC, DC, OT/PT, BS, T, AIDS, MND/OTI,
MD, NS – 32 WTE

CARDIFF, GLAMORGAN

*George Thomas Centre for Hospice
Care*
38 Ty Gwyn Road
Cyncoed
Cardiff
CF2 5JE
Tel. 0222 485345

Location: Cyncoed is a north-eastern
residential suburb of Cardiff
Contact: Centre Co-ordinator or
Chairman

HC, BS, T, AIDS, MND/OTI, NS – 2

CARLISLE, CUMBRIA

Carlisle and District Hospice Appeal
c/o 26 Longlands Road
Carlisle
CA3 9AD
Tel. Mr P. Whitley – 0228 31464/24431

Location: 1 mile south of Carlisle, off
Durdar Road, overlooking
Hammonds Pond

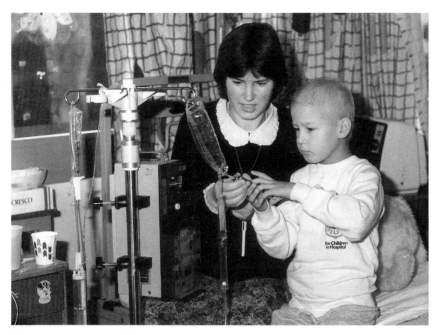

Helen Beswetherick, CLIC funded play-leader with Lee
at Bristol Childrens Hospital.

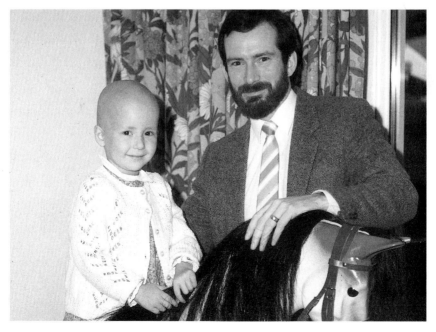

Katrina and her father in the playroom at CLIC House.

The CLIC chalet.

Catchment: East Cumbria Health
  Authority
Contacts: Mr P. Whitley, Chairman of
  Steering Committee, Trustee,
  member of Fund Raising Committee
  Dr M.A. Briggs, Trustee & member of
  Steering Committee

B – 12, HC, DC, BS, AIDS, MND/OTI

★ This is a *project* planned for
completion in September 1990.

  Macmillan Service
  Central Clinic
  Victoria Place
  Carlisle
  CA1 1HN
  Tel. 0228 36451

HC

CARMARTHEN, DYFED

  Macmillan Service
  West Wales General Hospital
  Glangwili
  Carmarthen
  SA31 3DE
  Tel. 0267 235151, ext 2071

Catchment: Carmarthen/Dinefwr
Contacts: Director of Nursing Services –
  Mr J. Power, West Wales General
  Hospital, Glangwili
  Macmillan nurse – Mrs C. Walters
Home-care contact: 0267 235151, ext 2071

HC, BS, AIDS, NS – 1

CASTLETROY, CO. LIMERICK

  Little Company of Mary Hospice
  Milford House
  Castletroy
  Tel. 010 353 61 43303

Contacts: Medical Director – Dr P.J.
  Kelly
  Matron – Sister Michael Sheehan
  Administrator – Sister Margaret
  Seymour

B – 20, HC, MND

CATERHAM, SURREY

  Harestone Marie Curie Home
  Harestone Drive
  Caterham
  CR3 6YQ
  Tel. 0883 42226

Location: Harestone Drive, off
  Harestone Valley Road, near
  Caterham station
Contact: Matron/Manager – Mrs M.R.
  Jupp

B – 24, BS, T, AIDS,* MD, NS – 30

* AIDS patients accepted if they have cancer.

CHALFORD HILL, GLOUCESTERSHIRE

  The Cotswold Care Project
  The Surgery
  Middle Hill
  Chalfont Hill
  GL6 8BD
  Tel. 0453 886868

Location: 1 mile north of A419, 4 miles
  east of Stroud
Contacts: Adminstrator – Mr Michael
  Tomlinson
  Chairman – Bishop John Gibbs

DC, BS, AIDS, MND/OTI

★ This is a *project*, planned to open in
autumn 1989. It will include volunteer
helpers to aid the local Macmillan nurses
and district nurses.

CHAPEL-EN-LE-FRITH, DERBYSHIRE

  High Peak Hospice
  137 Manchester Road
  Chapel-en-le-Frith
  Tel. 0298 22874

Catchment: 8-mile radius of Chapel-en-
  le-Frith
Contacts: Chairman – Rev. Betty
  Packham – 0298 25697
  Medical officer – Dr Simon Cocksedge
  – 0298 814236

★ Due to open in September 1989 with
social support and counselling. Medical
care to be included later.

CHEADLE, CHESHIRE

  St Ann's Hospice
  St Ann's Road North
  Heald Green
  Cheadle
  SK8 3SZ
  Tel. 061 437 8136

Location: ½ mile off A34 in Heald Green
Catchment: Central Manchester, South
  Manchester, Tameside, Oldham,
  Trafford, Stockport

Contacts: Administrator and Company
    Secretary – Mr J.T.M. Connolly
Matron – Mrs P. Birtwistle
Medical director – Dr M.P. Cole
Home-care contact: The patient's GP
    applies through the Hospice

B – 45, HC, OT/PT, BS, T, AIDS,* MND/OTI, MD,
NS – 57.5 WTE

*Will consider AIDS patients if associated with
terminal cancer.

CHEAM, SURREY

St Raphael's Hospice
London Road
North Cheam
SM3 9DX
Tel. 01 337 7475

Location: 2 miles north-east of Sutton
    town centre on the A24
Catchment: Merton & Sutton Health
    Authority
Contact: Medical director – Dr M.
    Wheildon
Home-care contact: Mrs Olive Crozier –
    01 337 7475

B – 10, HC, DC, OT/PT, BS, T, AIDS, MND/OTI,
MD, NS – 17 WTE

CHELMSFORD, ESSEX

Chelmsford Hospice
'Farleigh'
212 New London Road
Chelmsford
CM2 9AE
Tel. 0245 358130/269660

Location: to south of town 200 yards
    from Wood Street roundabout,
    A1083 off A12
Catchment: Mid-Essex Health Authority
Contacts: Administrator – Mr David
    Kliber
Matron – Mrs Janet Curmi
Medical Director – Dr David
    Frampton
Home-care contact: as above

B – 10, HC, DC, OT/PT, BS, T, NS – 20

CHELTENHAM, GLOUCESTERSHIRE

Macmillan Service
The Health Centre
Newton Road
Cheltenham
9LS 8BJ

Tel. 0242 525800

HC, HST

Sue Ryder Home
Leckhampton Court
Church Road
Leckhampton
Cheltenham
GL51 5XX
Tel. 0242 230199

Location: 1½ miles outside Cheltenham,
    just off A46
Catchment: Gloucestershire
Contacts: Matron – Mrs Dorothy Green
    Administrator – Mrs Avril Hastings
    Fund-Raising Co-ordinator – Mrs
        Gillian Rose
    Chairman – Mr C.J. Williams
Home-care contact: Mrs Avril Hastings –
    0242 230199

B – 38, HC, DC, OT/PT, BS, T, AIDS, MND/OTI,
MD, NS – 54

CHERTSEY, SURREY

Macmillan Nurse
St Peter's Hospital
Guildford Road
Chertsey
KT16 OPT
Tel. 0932 87 2000, ext 2312

Location: 1 mile from Chertsey town
    centre on main Chertsey-Woking
    road
Catchment: North-West Surrey
Contacts: Director of Nursing Services –
    Chris Eyes
    Macmillan Nurse – Anne Elton
    Macmillan nurse provides a service
        within St Peter's Hospital.

BS, T, AIDS, MND/OTI – provided at St Peter's
Hospital

CHESTER, CHESHIRE

Hospice of the Good Shepherd
Gordon Lane
Backford
Chester
CH2 4DG
Tel. 0244 851091

Contacts: Matron – Mrs A. Teaney
    Administrator – Mr A. Lambe
    Social Worker – Mrs E. Evans

B – 6, HC

CHESTERFIELD, DERBYSHIRE

Ashgate Hospice
Ashgate Road
Old Brampton
Chesterfield
S42 7JE
Tel. 0246 568801

Contacts: Medical Director – Dr Richard
    Atkinson
Matron – Mrs Mary Ryan
Administrator – Mrs Sue North

B – 14, DC, BS

Macmillan Service
Saltergate Health Centre
Saltergate
Chesterfield
Tel. 0246 211926

Location: town centre
Catchment: North Derbyshire
Contacts: Macmillan nurses – Michael
    Rogers & Linda Rudkin

HC, BS, AIDS, NS – 2

★ There are plans for a future day
hospice to be based in Chapel en le Frith.

CHESTER-LE-STREET, CO. DURHAM

Macmillan Service
Chester-le-Street Health Centre
Newcastle Road
Chester-le-Street
DH3
Tel. 0385 890990

HC, BS

CHICHESTER, SUSSEX

St Wilfrid's Hospice
Grosvenor Road
Chichester
PO19 2FP
Tel. 0243 775302

Location: junction south of Chichester
    by-pass on A286, ½ mile south of
    railway station
Contacts: Chairman of Board of
    Directors – Mr L. Thefaut
    Medical Director – Dr C.D. Lacey
    Matron – Mrs P. Aburrow
Home-care contact: Medical Director –
    Dr Lacey – 0243 775302

B – 9, HC, BS, MND, MD, NS – 15.5 WTE

★ The number of beds will shortly be
increased to 15.

CHORLEYWOOD, HERTS

Thorpedale Trust
Station approach
Chorleywood
WD3 5NE
Tel. 09278 4648

Contact: Dr P.G. Owston – 09278 3708

★ This is a *project*, hoping to open for
home care at the end of 1989 and for in-
patient care in mid-1990.

CHRISTCHURCH, DORSET

Macmillan Unit
Christchurch Hospital
Fairmile Road
Christchurch
BS23 2JX
Tel. 0202 486361

Contacts: Consultant in Continuing Care
    – Dr Fiona Randall
    Mrs Barbara Duffy – Nursing Officer
    Mrs Sue Oliver – Social Worker

B – 25, HC, DC, HST, BS, T

CLYDEBANK, STRATHCLYDE

St Margaret's Hospice
(The Irish Sisters of Charity)
East Barns Street
Clydebank
G81 1EG
Tel. 041 952 1141

Contacts: Medical Director – Dr Noel
    Harker
    Matron – Sister Rita Dawson

B – 25, HC

COCKERMOUTH, CUMBRIA

West Cumbria Hospice at Home
Shatton Hall
Cockermouth
CA13 9TL
Tel. 0900 822349

Catchment: The Health District of West
    Cumbria, i.e., the coastal strip
Contacts: Chairman and Medical
    Director – Dr E.B. Herd
    Hon. Sec. – Mr J.P. Frearson,
    Orchard Cottage, Main Street,
    Grey Southen, Cumbria

Director of Nursing Services – Mrs M.
Dowling, c/o Anne Burrow
Thomas Health Centre,
Workington, Cumbria
Home-care contacts: Margaret Dowling
– 0900 2244, ext 166; Christine
Mottram – 0946 5551, ext 249
(preferably 4.30–5.00 pm)

HC, T, AIDS, MND/OTI, MD, NS – 40 +

COLCHESTER, ESSEX

Macmillan Service
5 Cambridge Road
Colchester
CO3 3NS
Tel. 0206 571047

Catchment: North-East Essex Health
Authority
Contacts: Senior Nurse Manager – Mrs
D. Tait
Team Members – Mrs P. Buchan,
Mrs E. Powell, Mrs J. McKenna,
Mrs J. Jenkinson

HC, BS, T, AIDS, MND/OTI, NS – 4

St Helena Hospice
Barncroft Close
Highwoods
Colchester
CO4 4JU
Tel. 0206 845566

Location: 2 miles north of town centre on
Highwoods Estate off Ipswich Road
Contact: Hospice Director – Keith
Dallison

B – 15, DC, OT/PT, BS, T, AIDS, MND/OTI, MD,
NS – 28 WTE

COLERAINE, NORTHERN IRELAND

Macmillan Homecare Service
(NI Hospice)
Health Centre
Castlerock Road
Coleraine
BT51 3HP
Tel. 0265 42492

Catchment: Coleraine, Ballymoney &
Moyle District of Northern Health &
Social Services Board
Home-care contact: Macmillan sister –
0265 42492

HC, BS, T, AIDS, MND/OTI, NS – 3

CONSETT, DURHAM

North-West Durham Macmillan
Service
Consett Child Welfare Clinic
192 Medomsley Road
Consett
DH8 ONB
Tel. 0207 502420

Catchment: Derwentside
Contact: Miss Irene Mortimer, Unit
General Manager, Shotley Bridge
Hospital – 0207 503456

HC

★ Day care is planned.

CORK, CORK

Marymount Hospice
The Sisters of Charity
St Patrick's Hospital
Wellington Road
Cork
Tel. 021 501201

Location: city centre
Catchment: Southern Health Board Area
Contact: Matron – Sister J. Pius Keane
Home-care contact: Sister Dolores –
021 501201

B – 25, HC, BS, T, C, AIDS, MND, MD, NS – 15

COUNDON, CO. DURHAM

Macmillan Service
Health Centre
Victoria Lane
Coundon
DL14 8NL
Tel. 0388 605959

Catchment: South-West Durham –
Wearvally & Sedgefield District
Contacts: Macmillan nurses – Terry
Ricci, Elizabeth Flood

HC, NS – 2

COVENTRY, WARWICKSHIRE

Macmillan Service
Stoke Aldermoor Clinic
Aldermoor Lane
Aldermoor
Coventry
Tel. 0203 452473

HC

CRAWLEY, SUSSEX

St Catherine's Hospice
Malthouse Road
Crawley
RH10 6BH
Tel. 0293 547333

Contacts: Medical Director – Dr Bridget
  Jepson
  Matron – Mrs M. Fisher
  Bursar – Mr Iain Puddick

B – 28. HC. DC. BS. AIDS. *. T

* AIDS patients accepted if they have cancer.

CREWE, CHESHIRE

Macmillan Service
The Clinic Centre
85 Wheelock Street
Middlewich
Tel. 0606 845132; ansaphone 0270
  626662, ext 5235

HC

DARTFORD, KENT

Ellenor Foundation
Livingstone Community Hospital
East Hill
Dartford
DA1 1SA
Tel. 0322 21315

Location: ¼ mile east of town centre on
  A226
Catchment: Dartford & Gravesham
  Health District, i.e., north-west
  Kent
Contacts: Chairman – Mr Graham
  Perolls
  Adminstrator – Mr Tony Cornfield
  Senior Nurse Manager – Carol Stone
  Medical Director – Dr Jacqueline
  Fisher
Home-care contact: 0322 21315 (24 hour
  on call)

HST. HC. BS. T. AIDS. MND/OTI. MD. NS – 6

DARLINGTON,
CO. DURHAM

St Theresa's Hospice Project
(Darlington and District Hospice
  Movement)
41 Woodland Road
Darlington
DL3 7BJ
Tel. 0325 380634

Contact: Social Worker/Volunteers' Co-
  ordinator – Dorothy Davison

★ Volunteer hospice home-care sitting
service in operation. Purpose-built day-
care unit planned for 1990.

DAVENTRY,
NORTHAMPTONSHIRE

Macmillan Service
Daventry Health Centre
London Road
Daventry
Tel. 0327 70333

DENBIGH, CLWYD

Macmillan Service
Denbighshire Infirmary
Ruthin Road
Denbigh
LL16 3ES
Tel. 074571 2624

MiniMac (2 beds) + HC

DENNY, CENTRAL

Strathcarron Hospice
Randolph Hill
Denny
FK6 5JH
Tel. 0324 826222

Location: 8 miles south of Stirling, 1 mile
  west of Denny on B818
Catchment: Central Region plus
  Cumbernauld & Kilsyth
Contact: Administrator – John
  McFarlane
Home-care contact: Miss C.M. Parsons –
  0324 826222

B – 16. HC. DC. OT/PT. BS. T. MND/OTI. MD.
NS – 24 WTE

DERBY, DERBYSHIRE

*Nightingale Macmillan Continuing
  Care Unit*
Trinity Street
Derby
DE1 2RA
Tel. 0332 385012

Location: ½ mile south of Derby town
  centre on A6 opposite Derbyshire
  Royal Infirmary
Catchment: South Derbyshire Health
  Authority
Contact: Medical Director – Dr Michael
  Leveaux

B – 15, HC, DC, OT/PT, BS, T, AIDS,* MD, NS – 31

* AIDS patients accepted if they also have cancer.

DERRY, NORTHERN IRELAND

Foyle Hospice
9 Crawford Square
Derry
Tel. 0504 264917

HC

DONCASTER, YORKSHIRE

Doncaster Hospice Appeal
24 Imperial Crescent
Town Moor
Doncaster
DN2 5BU
Tel. 0302 349177/360664

★ Planning for day care and home care, plus 10–14 bed in-patient unit.

Symptom Control Team
c/o Dr T.J. Hughes
Doncaster Royal Infirmary
Armthorpe Road
DN4 6AD
Tel. 0302 366666, ext 516/599

Location: 1 mile east of town centre
Catchment: Doncaster Health District
Contact: Medical Adviser – Dr T.J. Hughes
Home-care contact: 0302 366666, ext 599/607

HST, HC, BS, MND/OTI, MD, NS – 2

★ There are plans for 8–10 beds.

DORCHESTER, DORSET

Macmillan Service
Edward Road
Dorchester
DT1 2HL
Tel. 0305 69898

Location: centre of Dorchester (office – no in-patient unit)
Catchment: West Dorset Health Authority area
Contact: Service Co-ordinator – Mrs Sara Milne
Home-care contact: 0305 69898

HC, DC, OT/PT, BS, T, AIDS, MND/OTI, MD, NS – 8

DORKING, SURREY

Hospice Home Care Surrey
Dorking Halls
Reigate Road
Dorking
RH4 1SG
Tel. 0306 881816

Contact: Medical Adviser – Dr B. Matthews

HC, MND, AIDS (volunteer service)

DOUGLAS, ISLE OF MAN

St Bridget's Hospice
Dorothy Pantin House
Kensington Road
Douglas
Tel. 0624 26530

Location: town centre
Catchment: Isle of Man
Contacts: Administrator – P.A.H. Vickers
Medical Director – Dr Hugh Revill
Matron – Mrs F.E.S. Calvert
Home-care contact: Sisters Pearson, Kinley or Hogg – 0624 26530

B – 7, HC, DC, OT, BS, T, AIDS, MND/OTI, MD, NS – 18.74 WTE

DUBLIN, REPUBLIC OF IRELAND

Our Lady's Hospice
P.O. Box 222
Harold's Cross
Dublin 6
Tel. 0001 972101/972839

Location: 2 miles from city centre
Catchment: Greater Dublin
Contact: Superior – S.R. Francis Rose

B – 44, HC, BS, T, C, AIDS, MND, MD, NS – 48

DUMFRIES, DUMFRIES & GALLOWAY

Alexandra Unit
Dumfries and Galloway Royal Infirmary
Bankend Road
Dumfries
DG1 2SD
Tel. 0387 53151, ext 347

Location: ½ mile south of town centre on road to Bankend village
Catchment: Dumfries & Galloway
Contacts: Medical Officer – Dr Lindsay Claire Martin

Medical Officer – Dr Craig Brown
Sister – Sister Ann Whitehead
Macmillan nurses – Jeanette Bain,
  Vivian Murray
Home-care contact: Dr L.C. Martin –
  0387 53151

B – 6, HC, OT/PT, BS, T, AIDS, MND/OTI, MD

DUNDEE, TAYSIDE

Roxburghe House
Royal Victoria Hospital
Jedburgh Road
Dundee
DD2 1SP
Tel. 0382 66246

Location: 2½ miles west of city centre,
  close by Ninewells Hospital
Catchment: Tayside & North Fife
Contacts: Sister in Charge – Sister E.
  Waugh
Locum Associate Specialist –
  Dr Barbara Dymock
Home-care contact: Mrs K. Brown –
  0382 66246

B – 25, HC, DC, C, AIDS, MND/OTI, MD, NS – 15

DURHAM, CO. DURHAM

St Cuthbert's Hospice
Park House Road
Merry Oaks
Durham
DH1 3QF
Tel. 091 386 1170

Location: on outskirts of Durham city
  (west), close by A167
Catchment: 10 miles radius of Durham
Contact: Adminstrator – Bryan Cooke

DC, OT/PT, BS, T, MD, NS – 1

★ A sitting service run by trained carers
is operated. An in-patient unit is planned
for the future.

EASTBOURNE, SUSSEX

Macmillan Service
'Taormina'
Princess Alice Hospital
Carew Road
Eastbourne
Tel. 0323 27997

HC

St Wilfrids Hospice (Eastbourne) Ltd
2 Mill Gap Road
Eastbourne
BN21 2HJ
Tel. 0323 642006/642056/644500

Location: ½ mile north of central station
Contacts: Medical Director –
  Dr J. Carey
Matron – Sister E. Lawrence-Newman
Secretary – Julia Wright
Home-care contact: 0323 27997

B – 7, HC, DC OT, BS, T, AIDS,* MND, MD,
NS – 16

* AIDS patients with cancer accepted for
home care.

EDENBRIDGE, KENT

Sevenoaks Hospice Link

Contact: Mrs R. Hargreaves
2 Redhill Cottages
Toys Hill
Edenbridge
Kent
TN8 6NP
Tel. 0732 75380

★ Planning for day-care centre.

EDINBURGH, LOTHIAN

Fairmile Marie Curie Home
Frogston Road West
Edinburgh
EH10 7DR
Tel. 031 445 2141

Location: part of Fairmile Head off the
  ring road
Contact: Matron/Manager – Mrs D.M.
  Innes

B – 38, DC, OT/PT, BS, T, AIDS,* MD, NS – 42

* AIDS patients accepted if they have cancer.

Milestone Venture Trust
64 Broughton Street
Edinburgh
EH1 3SA
Tel. 031 557 6580

Contact: Dr Jamie Inglis

★ A 20-bed in-patient unit planned for
January 1990, with home care to follow,
for people with HIV and AIDS.

St Columba's Hospice
Challenger Lodge
Boswall Road
Edinburgh
Tel. 031 551 1381

Location: 1 mile north-east of city centre,
    overlooking River Forth
Contacts: Administrator – Major David
    Meehan
    Medical Director – Dr Derek Doyle
    Nursing Director – Mrs Jeanie
    Simpson

B – 30, HC, DC, OT/PT, BS, T, MND/OTI, MD, NS
– 41 WTE

ELGIN, GRAMPIAN

Grampian West Macmillan Service
Health Centre
Maryhill
Elgin
IV30 1A1
Tel. 0343 3141, ext 240

Location: ½ mile west of Elgin town
    centre
Catchment: Morayshire
Contacts: Director of Nursing Services –
    Miss J. Fraser
    Macmillan Charge Nurse – Kenneth
    M. Ferguson
Home-care contact: Kenneth M.
    Ferguson – 0343 3141, ext 240

HC, BS, T, ND/OTI, NS – 1

EPPING, ESSEX

Macmillan Service
St Margaret's Hospital
Epping
CM16 6TN
Tel. 0378 77322

★ Breast-care nurse.

ESHER, SURREY

The Princess Alice Hospital
West End Lane
Esher
KT10 8NA
Tel. 0372 68811

Location: ¾ mile west of town centre on
    A244
Catchment: 10-mile radius of Esher
Contacts: Administrative Director –
    Andrew Jones

Nursing director – Tony Wingett
Medical Director – Dr Andrew Hoy
Home-care contact: Dr Andrew Hoy –
    0372 68811

B – 26, HC, DC, OT/PT, BS, T, AIDS, MND/OTI,
MD, NS – 39 WTE

EXETER, DEVON

Hospiscare
Mowbray Cottage
Butts Road
Heavitree
Exeter
EX2 5BE
Tel. 0392 54281 – general;
    0392 56391 – nurses

Location: 1½ miles from city centre on
    main road to the east en route for
    M5; ¼ mile from District General
    Hospital
Catchment: area covered by Exeter
    General Practitioner List; also
    Budleigh Salterton, Sidmouth and
    Exmouth
Contacts: Chairman – Dr J.F. Searle
    Company Secretary – Mrs A.M. Wills
    Senior Sister – Mrs J. Pettitt
Home-care contact: 0392 54281 or 56391
    All referrals taken but no visits made
    without support of GP and
    Community Nurse

HC, BS, T, C, AIDS, MND, NS – 5

★ A 12-bed in-patient unit plus day care
planned for late 1990.

EXMOUTH, DEVON

Macmillan Service
Hospice Care
Exmouth Hospital
Claremount Grove
Exmouth
Tel. 0395 264089

HC

FARNHAM, SURREY

Phyllis Tuckwell Memorial Hospice
Waverley Lane
Farnham
GU9 8BL
Tel. 0252 725814

Location: south of the railway station on
    the B3001

Catchment: North-East Hampshire, West Surrey, South-West Surrey – Basingstoke & North Hampshire
Contacts: Hon. House Governor – Lieut.-Colonel A.M. Cooper
Matron – Miss M.E. Rouse
Hon. Medical Director – Dr M. Salzman

B – 26, BS, T, AIDS, MND/OTI, MD, NS – 28 WTE

★ A day hospice is planned for the end of 1989.

GALWAY, GALWAY

Galway Hospice Service
9 Prospect Hill
Galway
Tel. 091 21717

Contacts: Dr R. Latey
Chairman – Dr P.O. O'Congavie
Secretary – Mrs K. Farrell

★ This *project*, due to open in January 1990, is planning home-care service for Galway city and county.

GATESHEAD, TYNE & WEAR

Macmillan Service
Gateshead Health Centre
Prince Consort Road
Gateshead
NE8 1NB
Tel. 091 478 3711

HC, NS – 2

GLASGOW, STRATHCLYDE

Macmillan Service
Radiotherapy Out Patients Unit
Belvedere Hospital
London Road
Glasgow
G31 4BG
Tel. 041 554 1855

Hunters Hill Marie Curie Home
Belmont Road
Glasgow
G21 3AY
Tel. 041 558 2555

Location: Springburn area, 3 miles north of city centre
Contacts: Matron/Manager – Miss S. Bett
Medical Director – Dr J. Welsh
Deputy Director – Dr J.S. Adam

B – 44, DC, OT/PT, BS, T, AIDS,*, MND, NS – 71

* AIDS patients accepted if they have cancer.

Prince & Princess of Wales Hospice
71–73 Carlton Place
Glasgow
G5 9TD
Tel. 041 429 5599

Contacts: Medical Director – Dr Anne J.J. Gilmore
Administrator – Mr A.K. Harrison
Matron – Miss Johanna Ritchie
Social worker – Janet Miller

HC, DC, BS, MND

★ Mrs Anne McBryan – 24-hour telephone-answering service for health professionals in Greater Glasgow.

The Macmillan Hospital Support Team
Victoria Infirmary
Langside
Glasgow
G42 9TY
Tel. 041 649 4545, ext 5454/5463

Location: south-east of Glasgow, 2 miles from city centre
Catchment: referrals only from within the hospital
Contacts: Dr Margaret M. Hutton
Sister Margaret C. Sneddon

HST, T, AIDS,* MND/OTI,* MD, NS – 1

* If referred.

GLOUCESTER, GLOUCESTERSHIRE

Gloucester Macmillan Nursing Service
162 Barnwood Road
Gloucester
GL4 7JX
Tel. 0452 371022

Location: 2 miles from Gloucester city centre
Catchment: Gloucester city, Stroud, Forest of Dean, Cheltenham
Contact: team leader of Macmillan nurses – Mrs V. Gage – 0452 371022

HC, BS, T, AIDS, MND/OTI, NS – 5

GODALMING, SURREY

Macmillan Service
Milford Hospital
Godalming
Tel. 04868 4411

HC

GRANTHAM, LINCOLNSHIRE

Community Macmillan Nursing Service
Grantham Health Clinic
St Catherines Road
Grantham
Tel. 0476 590805

Location: Grantham town centre, behind cinema
Contact: Community Macmillan nurse – Cathy Jones – 0476 590805

HC, BS, NS – 1

Macmillan Service
Grantham Hospital
101 Manthorpe Road
Grantham
NG31 6BR
Tel. 0476 65232

GREAT YARMOUTH, NORFOLK

Macmillan Nursing Service
James Paget Hospital
Lowestoft Road
Gorleston
Great Yarmouth
NR31 6LA
Tel. 0493 600611, ext 647

Location: southern edge of Gorleston on A12
Catchment: Great Yarmouth & Waveney Health District (including Great Yarmouth, Caister, Lowestoft, Southwold, Halesworth, Beccles, Bungay)
Contact: Medical Director – Dr W.G. Notcutt
Home-care contact: Secretary to the Macmillan Nursing Service, James Paget Hospital, 0493 600611, ext 647

HC, HST, BS, T, AIDS, MND/OTI, MD, NS – 3

GREENOCK, STRATHCLYDE

Ardgowan Hospice Ltd
Nelson Street
Greenock
Renfrewshire
PA15 1TS
Tel. 0475 26830/81339

Contacts: Medical Director – Dr S. McKechnie
Matron – Mrs Jean Galbraith

Administrator – Mr David McMurray

HC, DC, BS, MND, AIDS, T

GRIMSBY, HUMBERSIDE

Support Sister
District General Hospital
Scartho Road
Grimsby
DN33 2BA
Tel. 0472 74111

Location: 2 miles south-west of town centre
Catchment: Grimsby
Contact: Support Sister – Freda Dalkin – 0472 74111

HC, HST, BS, T, AIDS, MND/OTI, NS – 1 (will increase to 3)

St Andrew's Hospice
The Beeches
42 Waltham Road
Scartho
Grimsby
DN33 2LX
Tel. 0472 79722

Catchment: Grimsby Health Authority – Grimsby & Cleethorpes, surrounding villages & North Lincolnshire
Contacts: Hospice General Manager – Mrs Ros Bishop
Medical Director – Dr Paul Heath
Nursing Team Leader – Miss Alison Gyte

B – 5, DC, OT/PT, BS, T, MND/OTI, MD, NS – 11.29 WTE

★ A home-care team is planned and is awaiting financial resources. It is also hoped to accept AIDS patients when finances are available.

GROUVILLE, JERSEY

Jersey Hospice Care
Clarkson House
Rue de la Haie du Puits
Grouville
Jersey
Tel. 0534 53130

Location: 4 miles east of St Helier, ½ mile from Gorey village
Catchment: Jersey
Contact: Senior Sister – Mrs M.M. McGovern
Home-care contact: 0534 53130

B – 5, HC, DC, OT/PT, BS, T, MND, NS – 7+

GUILDFORD, SURREY

Macmillan Hospital Support Nurse
Royal Surrey County Hospital
Edgerton Road
Guildford
GU2 5XX
Tel. 0483 571122

Contact: Macmillan Hospital Support
Nurse – Mrs Jean Evans

★ Covers Royal Surrey County Hospital
and St Luke's Hospital.

GUISBOROUGH, CLEVELAND

Macmillan Service
Guisborough Health Centre
Bow Street
Guisborough
TS14 7AA
Tel. 0287 35436

HC

HALIFAX, WEST YORKSHIRE

Overgate Hospice
30 Hullen Edge Road
Elland
Halifax
HX5 0QX
Tel. 0422 79151

Location: 1 mile west of M62, junction 23
Catchment: Calderdale Metropolitan
Borough
Contacts: Medical Director – Dr S.F.
Spencer
Matron – Mrs J. Thompson
Hon. Secretary – Mrs S. Rorke
Hon. Treasurer – Mr P. Taylor
Home-care contact: Macmillan Nursing
Service – 0422 45911

B – 8, BS, MD, NS – 21

Macmillan Service
Frank Lee Unit
Royal Halifax Infirmary
Free School Lane
Halifax
HX1 2YP
Tel. 0422 345911

Catchment: Calderdale
Contacts: Director of Nursing Services –
Mr Peter Davidson
Senior Nurse Manager – Mrs C. Short

HC, BS, T, AIDS, NS – 3

HARLOW, ESSEX

Princess Alexandra Hospital
Hamstel Road
Harlow
Essex
Tel. 0279 26791

Contact: Macmillan Nurse – Monica
Birchall

★ Macmillan nurse working in hospital
plus 2 community nurses.

HARROGATE, NORTH YORKSHIRE

Macmillan Service
Harrogate General Hospital
Knaresborough Road
Harrogate
HG2 7ND
Tel. 0423 885959

HC

St Michael's Hospice
35 Oatlands Drive
Harrogate
HG2 8PU
Tel. 0432 811089/880783

Contact: Matron – Jane Ranson

B – 5

HARROW, MIDDLESEX

Continuing Care Team, Harrow
Florence Nightingale House
Harrow Hospital
Roxeth Hill
Harrow
HA1 0JX
Tel. 01 864 5432, ext 283/278/272

Location: 1 mile from Northwick Park
Hospital, 1 mile from Harrow Town
station
Catchment: Harrow Health District
Contact: Team Leader – Irene Brown

HC, BS, AIDS, NS – 3

HARTLEPOOL, CLEVELAND

Hartlepool Hospice Ltd
Alice House
13 Hutton Avenue
Hartlepool
TS26 9PW
Tel. 0429 221503

Location: town centre, ¼ mile west of
main A689 road

Catchment: Hartlepool Health
Authority, including Greatham,
Peterlee & Blackhall
Contact: Company Secretary – Mr G.J.
Owen
Home-care contact: Sister B.A. Magee,
Sister B. Bateman – 0429 221503

HC, DC, OT/PT, BS, AIDS, MND/OTI, NS – 3

★ An in-patient unit with 7 beds is
planned to open in late 1989/early 1990.

HASTINGS, EAST SUSSEX

Macmillan Nursing Service
Hastings Health Authority
13 Holmesdale Gardens
Hastings
TN34 1LY
Tel. 0424 714805

Catchment: Hastings Health Authority
Contact: Macmillan nurse – Linda
Hodgson

HC, BS, T, C, AIDS, MND, NS – 2

HAVERFORDWEST, DYFED

Macmillan Service
Meyler House
11 Albany Terrace
St Thomas Green
Haverfordwest
SA61 1QP
Tel. 0437 67801

HC

The Paul Sartori Foundation
11 Albany Terrace
St Thomas Green
Haverfordwest
SA61 1RH
Tel. 0437 3223

Catchment: The old county of Pembroke
Contact: Administrator – W.A.H. Smith
Home-care contact: Miss M.J. Thomas –
0437 3223

HC, AIDS, MND/OTI, NS – 6

HAYES, MIDDLESEX

Victoria Lodge
23 Victoria Lane
Harlington
Hayes

Contact: Dr Ellis

★ Have purchased a building.

HAYLE, CORNWALL

St Julia's Hospice
St Michael's Hospital
4 Trelissick Road
Hayle
TR27 4HY
Tel. 0736 753234

Location: western end of Hayle, 1 mile
south-west of station off B3302
Catchment: Camborne, westward to
Lands End
Contacts: Sister Superior – Sister
Catherine Murray
Matron – Sister Maureen McNally
Administrator – Mr Dennis Seager

B – 4, DC, OT/PT, BS, T, AIDS, MND/OTI, MD, NS
– 6.4 WTE

★ The day hospice is planned to open in
autumn 1989 and there may be a future
increase of in-patient beds to 12.

HEBBURN, TYNE & WEAR

Macmillan Service
Hebburn Health Centre
Campbell Park Road
Hebburn
Tel. 091 428 0241

HEMEL HEMPSTEAD, HERTFORDSHIRE

Macmillan Service
Halsey House
Hemel Hempstead General Hospital
Hemel Hempstead
HP2 4AD
Tel. 0442 3141, ext 2153

HC

HENLEY-ON-THAMES, OXFORDSHIRE

Sue Ryder Home
Nettlebed
Henley-on-Thames
RG9 5DF
Tel. 0491 641384

Location: 3 miles north-west of Henley,
on the A423 Oxford road
Catchment: West Berkshire – High
Wycombe Health District
Contacts: Matron – Mrs Marilyn Cottrell
Administrator – Wing-Cdr J.A.
Thomson
Medical Officer – Dr A.J. Pim

Home-care contact: Sister Connie Henry
– 0491 641384 (9–10.00 am)

B – 25, HC, DC, OT/PT, BS, T, AIDS,* MND,
NS – 37 WTE

* Only those with malignant disease.

HERNE BAY, KENT

The Buddhist Hospice Trust
P.O. Box 51
Herne Bay
CT6 6TP

Catchment: Britain
Contact: Dennis Sibley, 17 Cavendish
    Place, Newport, Isle of Wight PO3
    5AE. Tel – 0983 521297

★ Aims to provide physical care,
emotional support and spiritual
counselling from a Buddhist perspective
for those who are dying or bereaved –
both Buddhists and non-Buddhists. Plans
to build a house of retreat.

Macmillan Service
Queen Victoria Memorial Hospital
King Edward Avenue
Herne Bay
Tel. 0227 373246, ext 216

Catchment: Canterbury & Thanet
Contact: Director of Nursing Services
Home-care contact: 0227 373246, ext 216

HC, BS, NS – 1

HINCKLEY, LEICESTERSHIRE

Macmillan Service
Hinckley Health Centre
Hill Street
Hinckley
Tel. 0455 251200

HC, NS – 1

HITCHIN, HERTFORDSHIRE

Macmillan Service
Laburnum House
Hitchin Hospital
Hitchin
SG5 2LH
Tel. 0462 422444

HC

HOLME ON SPALDING MOOR, EAST YORKSHIRE

Sue Ryder Home
Holme Hall
Holme on Spalding Moor
Humberside
Tel. 0430 860904

Contact: Sister in Charge – Sister
    Stephenson

MND/OTI

HOLT, NORFOLK

Macmillan Service
Kelling Hospital
High Kelling
Holt
NR25 6QA
Tel. 0263 71333, ext 216

HC

HOLYWELL, CLWYD

Macmillan Service
Greenfields Clinic
Holywell
Tel. 0352 712468

HC

HUDDERSFIELD, WEST YORKSHIRE

Kirkwood Hospice
21 Albany Road
Dalton
Huddersfield
HD5 9UY
Tel. 0484 512101

Contacts: Medical Director –
    Dr Elizabeth Higgins
    Matron – John Murgatroyd
    Social Worker – Mrs Hilary Turner

B – 11, DC, AIDS, MD

HULL, HUMBERSIDE

Macmillan Service
Hull Royal Infirmary
Anlaby Road
Hull
HU3 2KZ
Tel. 0482 28541

North Humberside Hospice Project
Dove House
Beverley Road
Hull
HU6 7NH
Tel. 0482 446782

Contacts: Medical Director – Dr Sean
   Dunn
Administrator – Mrs Reggie Browne
Head Social Worker – Mrs V.
   Horspool

HC, DC, BS, HST

★ In-patient unit opening 1990.

ILFORD, ESSEX

Macmillan Service
Manford Way Health Centre
40 Foremark Close
Hainault
Ilford
IG6 3HS
Tel. 01 500 9954

HC

ILKLEY, WEST YORKSHIRE

Ardenlea Marie Curie Home
Queens Drive
Ilkley
LS29 8QR
Tel. 0943 607505

Location: Queens Drive is an extension
   of Queens Road, just south of Ilkley
   railway station
Contact: Matron/Manager – Miss S.
   Bradley

B – 27, DC, OT/PT, BS, T, AIDS,* MD, NS – 34

* AIDS patients accepted if they have cancer.

INVERNESS, HIGHLAND

Highland Hospice
1 Bishop's Road
Inverness
IV3 5SB
Tel. 0463 243132

Location: in Inverness town, opposite the
   theatre & alongside the river
Catchment: the Highland region
Contacts: Manager – Mrs Lyn Forbes
   Matron – Mrs Margo Deaves
   Medical Director – Dr Edward
   Barrington-Ward
Home-care contact: Mr Brian Hunter,
   Miss Wilma Mair – 0463 243132

B – 10, HC, DC, OT/PT, BS, T, AIDS, MND/OTI,
MD, NS – 19 WTE

Macmillan Service
Raigmore Hospital
Surgical Floor
Raigmore
Inverness
Tel. 0463 234151

★ Hospital based, liaising with
community nurses.

IPSWICH, SUFFOLK

Macmillan Service
Allington Clinic
427 Woodbridge Road
Ipswich
IP4 4ER
Tel. 0473 720931

HC

St Elizabeth Hospice
565 Foxhall Road
Ipswich
IP3 8LX
Tel. 0473 727776

Location: 2 miles from town centre off
   the ring road A12/A45
Contacts: Hospice Manager – Mr Ron
   Cullen
   Matron – Mrs Susan Avens
Home-care contact: Voluntary Service
   Organizer – 0473 713931

B – 10, DC, OT/PT, BS, T, AIDS,* MND/OTI,*
NS – 19.16

* It is expected that the majority of patients will have
advanced cancer but other patients will be accepted if
they have been diagnosed as terminally ill. Home care
consists of a volunteer sitting service which is readily
available.

★ This is a *project*, due to open on
1 November 1989.

ISLEWORTH, MIDDLESEX

Clinical Nurse Specialist
West Middlesex University Hospital
Isleworth
TW7 6AF
Tel. 01 560 2121

★ Hospital referrals only.

JARROW, TYNE & WEAR

South Tyneside Special Care Team
Community Nursing Service
South Tyneside Health Authority
Monkton Hall Hospital
Monkton Village
Jarrow
NE32 5NN
Tel. 091 428 0241

Contacts: Nurse Manager – Mrs M.
Noble
Senior Nurse Manager – Mrs S.E.
Rowan
Home-care contact: Mrs M. Noble –
091 428 0241

HC, BS, T, AIDS

**JOHNSTONE,
STRATHCLYDE**

St Vincent's Hospice
North Road
Johnstone
PA5 8NE
Tel. 0505 31858

Location: 3 miles from Paisley, turn off
on Beith road.
Catchment: Johnstone, Paisley, Barrhead
Contact: Sister Margaret

B – 8, MND/OTI, NS – 25

**KEIGHLEY, WEST
YORKSHIRE**

Manorlands
Sue Ryder Home
Oxenhope
Keighley
BD22 9RX
Tel. 0535 42308

Location: near Haworth, 3 miles from
A629 Halifax-Keighley road
Catchment: Bradford Health District &
Airedale Health District
Contacts: Matron – Mrs Sheila Brothwell
Hon. Medical Consultant – Dr Jack
Ward
Home-care contacts: Sister Janet Lodge,
Sister Janet Munro – 0535 42308

B – 20, HC, OT/PT, AIDS, NS – 22 WTE

KENDAL, CUMBRIA

Macmillan Service
Blackhall Road Health Centre
Blackhall Road
Kendal
Tel. 0539 27564

**KETTERING,
NORTHAMPTONSHIRE**

Macmillan Service
Stockburn Memorial Home
London Road
Kettering
NN15 7QG
Tel. 0536 410360/1/2/3

HC

**KIDDERMINSTER,
WORCESTERSHIRE**

Terminal Care Support Group
Kidderminster General Hospital
Bewdley Road
Kidderminster
DY11 6RJ
Tel. 0562 823424

HC, MND, AIDS

★ Referrals from within hospital only.

KILKENNY, KILKENNY

Carlow/Kilkenny Home Care Team
Ltd
St Luke's Hospital
Kilkenny
Tel. 056 21133

Catchment: Carlow and Kilkenny
counties
Contact: Nurse K. Murry

HC, BS, MD, NS – 2+

**KILMARNOCK,
STRATHCLYDE**

Continuing Care Unit (Surgical
Oncology)
Crosshouse Hospital
Crosshouse
Kilmarnock
Tel. 0563 21133, ext 3418

Location: 2 miles from Kilmarnock on
the Irvine road
Catchment: North Ayrshire (surgical
patients only)
Contacts: Consultant Surgeon – Mr W.
Miller
Director of Nursing Services – Mr J.
Welch
Clinical Nurse Manager – Mrs A.
Luney
Unit Sister – Sister F. Grant
Home-care contact: Sister P. Stracey –
0563 21133, ext 3418

★ A Macmillan sister liaises with the unit and the patients, but the unit as such is considered to be a continuing-care unit rather than a hospice.

KING'S LYNN, NORFOLK

Macmillan Service
Queen Elizabeth Hospital
Gayton Road
King's Lynn
Tel. 0553 766266

HC – referrals from hospital and community.

West Norfolk Home Hospice Support
Tapping House
22a Common Road
Snettisham
King's Lynn
PE31 7PE
Tel. 0485 43163

Contacts: Co-ordinator – Mrs Pin
   Armitage
Secretaries – Mrs Sharon May, Mrs
   Kim Bowett
Home-care contact: Mrs Pin Armitage –
   0485 43163

DC, OT/PT, BS, T, AIDS, MND/OTI, MD, NS – 1

★ This unit also offers a sitting service.

KINGSTON, SURREY

Macmillan Continuing Care Team
Averill Lodge
Kingston Hospital
Galsworthy Road
Kingston
KT2 7QB
Tel. 01 546 7711, ext 435

Catchment: Kingston & Esher Area
   Health Authority
Contacts: Medical Director – Dr H.
   Leonard
Nursing Officer – Miss E. McConnell

HST, HC, BS, MD, NS – 6

KIRKCALDY, FIFE

Fife Health Board Macmillan Service
Kirkcaldy Health Centre
Whytemans Brae
Kirkcaldy
KY1 2NA
Tel. 0592 266271

Catchment: Fife
Contact: Associate Physician – Dr G.M.
   Halliday

HC, BS, AIDS, MND/OTI, NS – 4

LANCASTER, LANCASHIRE

St John's Hospice
Lancaster Road
Slyne
Lancaster
LA2 6AW
Tel. 0524 382538

Location: 1 mile north of Lancaster city
   centre on A6
Contacts: Matron – Sister Aine Cox
   Administrator – Mrs B. Farrer

B – 28, DC, OT/PT, BS, T, AIDS, MND/OTI, MD, NS – 28

LANCHESTER, CO. DURHAM

Macmillan Service
Maiden Law Hospital
Hawden Bank
Lanchester
Tel. 0207 502420

LEAMINGTON SPA, WARWICKSHIRE

Macmillan Service
Crown Way Clinic
Crown Way
Leamington Spa
CV32 7SF
Tel. 0926 332242

HC

LEATHERHEAD, SURREY

Rainbow Trust
Dove Cottage
16 The Glade
Fetcham
Leatherhead
KT22 9TH
Tel. 0372 50156

Location: 2 miles south-east of
   Leatherhead
Contact: Bernadette Cleary

B – 3, HC, BS, T, AIDS, MND/OTI

★ Rainbow Trust cares for children with terminal illness and their families.

LEEDS, WEST YORKSHIRE

Macmillan Service
Kirkstall Clinic
Morriss lane
Leeds
LS5 3DB
Tel. 0532 759954

Catchment: Leeds Western Health
   Authority

Contact: Senior Nurse – Miss J. Palmer
– 0532 444831
Home-care contact: – 0532 633172

HC, BS, T, C, AIDS, NS – 3

St Gemma's Hospice
329 Harrogate Road
Moortown
Leeds
LS17 6QD
Tel. 0532 693231/2/3

Location: 3½ miles from Leeds city
centre on the Harrogate Road
Catchment: Leeds East & Leeds West
District Health Authority areas; also
Bradford, Harrogate, Pontefract &
other areas as required
Contacts: Director of Nursing Services –
Sister Mary Sloan
Medical Director – Dr John Sinson
Administrator – Canon Joseph Lyons
Home-care contact: Mrs U. Martin, Mrs
J. Fisher – 0532 693231

B – 45, HC, DC, OT/PT, BS, T, AIDS.* MND/OTI,
MD, NS – 75 WTE

* AIDS patients will be considered for in-patient care if
they have cancer. There is already provision for AIDS
patients in Leeds.

Macmillan Service
St James University Hospital
Beckett Street
Leeds
LS9 7TF
Tel. 0532 433144

HC

Macmillan Service
Seacroft and Killingbeck Hospitals
York road
Leeds
LS14 6UH
Tel. 0532 648164

Wheatfields Hospice
Grove Road
Headingley
Leeds
LS6 2AE
Tel. 0532 787249

Location: 1 mile north-east from city
centre – just off A660
Catchment: mainly Leeds but also
surrounding areas
Contacts: Hospice Manager – Ms Maire
O'Donnell
Clinical Nurse Manager – Ms Angela
Cresswell

Administrator – Mrs Anita Mountain
Social worker – Ms Maureen Wilson
Home-care contact: Home-Care Team –
0532 787249

B – 22, HC, BS, C, AIDS, MD, NS – 33 WTE

LEICESTER, LEICESTERSHIRE

Macmillan Service
Blaby Hospital
Hospital Lane
Leicester
Tel. 0533 774333

HC

Macmillan Service
Coalville Health Centre
1 Market Street
Coalville
Leicester
Tel. 0530 510510

HC, AIDS

Macmillan Service
Leicester General Hospital
Gwendolen Road
Leicester
LE5 4PW
Tel. 0533 730222

★ Referrals from hospital only.

The Leicestershire Hospice
Groby Road
Leicester
LE3 9QE
Tel. 0533 313771

Location: 2 miles from city centre on A50
Catchment: Leicestershire & Rutland
Contacts: Medical Director – Dr S.
Ahmedzai
Matron – Mrs Bronwen Biswas
General Manager – Mr Michael
Archer

B – 25, DC, BS, OT/PT, MND, T, NS – 28.5 WTE

★ In-patient care available for AIDS
patients.

LOROS Day Care Centre
Manor Croft
147 Ratcliffe Road
Leicester
Tel. 0533 707339

Contact: Officer in Charge – Mrs Phina
Johnson

DC, OT/PT

LEIGH, LANCASHIRE

Macmillan Service
Wigan Hospice
(Leigh Home Care)
Bradshaw Gate
Leigh
Tel. 0942 260195

LETCHWORTH, HERTFORDSHIRE

The North Hertfordshire Hospice
Baldock Road
Letchworth
SG6 1QU
Tel. 0462 421323

Location: 1 mile from Letchworth station, 1 mile from A1 (M)
Catchment: North Herts District Health Authority – Knebworth, Stevenage, Hitchin, Letchworth, Baldock & Royston plus villages
Home-care contact: Macmillan Office, Hitchin Hospital – 0462 422444

BS, T, volunteer visiting service

★ Plans for 15-bed in-patient unit, with day-care facilities, to open in spring 1990.

LETTERKENNY, CO. DONEGAL

Foyle Hospice – Donegal Branch
Letterkenny General Hospital
Letterkenny
Tel. 074 22022, ext 236

Location: ½ mile from town centre on Kilmacrennan Road. Office in Nurses' Home, General Hospital
Catchment: County Donegal at present, but expected to become restricted to north Donegal as caseload grows
Contact: Sister Helen MacMahon

HC, BS, AIDS, MND, MD,* NS – 1

* MD is based at Foyle Hospice – Derry Branch.

LEYLAND, LANCASHIRE

Macmillan Service
Leyland Clinic
Yewlands Drive
Leyland
Tel. 0772 422378

★ Works in conjunction with St Catherine's Hospice, Preston.

LICHFIELD, STAFFORDSHIRE

St Giles Hospice
Fisherwick Road
Whittington
Lichfield
WS14 9LH
Tel. 0543 432031

Location: 3 miles south of Lichfield off the A51
Catchment: 25 miles radius of St Giles
Contacts: Medical Director – Mr J.H. Taylor
Director of Nursing Services – Mrs M.P. Ballard
Bursar – Mrs A.R. Newton
Home-care contact: Senior Nurse, Home Care – 0543 432031

B – 15, HC, DC, OT/PT, BS, T, AIDS, MND/OTI, MD, NS – 32.2 WTE

★ Beds will increase to 18 in 1990.

LINCOLN, LINCOLNSHIRE

St Barnabas Hospice
36 Nettleham Road
Lincoln
LN2 1RE
Tel. 0522 511566

Contacts: Medical Director – Dr R.A. Catterall
Matron – Miss Jane Burley
General Manager – Mr K.S. Davidson
Social Worker – Mr Peter Day

B – 11, HC, DC, BS, T, C, AIDS, MND, MD, NS – 20+ 6 HC

LIVERPOOL, MERSEYSIDE

Macmillan Service
Broadgreen Hospital
Thomas Drive
Liverpool
L14 3LB
Tel. 051 228 4878

HC

The Continuing Care Service
District Headquarters
Fazakerley Hospital
Long Moor Lane
Liverpool
L9 7AL
Tel. 051 525 3622, ext 2336

HC, BS, MND, NS – 2

Macmillan Service
Royal Liverpool Hospital
Prescot Street
Liverpool
L7 8XP
Tel. 051 709 0141

★ Referrals from within hospital only.

St Joseph's Hospice Association –
Hospice International
La Casa de San Jose
Ince Road
Thornton
Liverpool
L23 4UE
Tel. 051 924 3812/3/7871

Location: 7 miles from Liverpool, 6 miles
from Southport on A565
Catchment: Merseyside (but not
restricted to this area)
Contacts: Director – Father Francis
O'Leary
Nursing Superintendent – Mrs
Filomena O'Leary
Home-care contact: Mr Peter Heron –
36 71057

B – 45, HC, DC, OT/PT, BS, T, MND/OTI, MD,
NS – 107

Macmillan Service
Community Headquarters
Sefton General Hospital
Smithdown Road
Liverpool
L15 2HE
Tel. 051 733 5234 (direct line with
answerphone); 733 4020, ext 2574

Location: within hospital complex –
1½ – 2 miles east from city centre
on A562
Catchment: Liverpool
Contact: Nurse Manager – Miss K.
Williams, Deputy Director of
Community – 051 733 4020, ext 2301

HC, BS, T, AIDS, MND/OTI, NS – 4

Sunnybank Marie Curie Home
Speke Road
Woolton
Liverpool
L25 8QA
Tel. 051 428 1395/6

Location: Speke Road is in the centre of
Woolton village
Contact: Matron/Manager –
Mrs P. Carter

B – 30, DC, OT/PT, BS, T, AIDS,* MD, NS – 35

* Aids patients accepted if they have cancer.

LIVINGSTON, LOTHIAN

West Lothian Macmillan Service
Dedridge Health Centre
Nigel Rise
Dedridge
Livingston
EH54 6QQ
Tel. 0506 414586

Location: south side of Livingston in
Dedridge West
Catchment: West Lothian District
Contacts: Sister Morna Rutherford
Sister Karen Ivory

HC, BS, T, C, AIDS, NS – 2

LLANDUDNO, GWYNEDD

St David's Hospice Foundation –
Aberconwy Appeal
Aberconwy Community Office
Oxford Road
Llandudno
Tel. 0492 860011

Contact: Macmillan nurse – Valerie
Whittington

HC, BS, NS – 1

★ One Macmillan nurse is already
working but the Appeal hopes to provide
a full home-care team, day care and in-
patient care in the future.

LONDON, EAST

Macmillan Support Team
Central Nursing Office
The London Hospital
London E1 1BB
Tel. 01 377 7282

Location: opposite Whitechapel
underground station
Catchment: the London Hospital
(Whitechapel), the London Hospital
(Mile End)
Contact: Director of Nursing Services –
Miss B. Faulkner
Home-care contact: 01 377 7282 initially

HST, BS, T, AIDS, NS – 2

Mildmay Mission Hospital
Hackney Road
London
E2 7NA
Tel. 01 739 2331

Location: Shoreditch – 100 yards along Hackney Road (south side) from Shoreditch Parish Church
Catchment: no referral boundaries in theory but practical considerations may rule out those from too far away
Contacts: Unit General Manager/ Director of Nursing Services – Mrs Ruth Sims
Medical Director/Director of Service Planning – Dr Veronica Moss
Administrator – Mr John Cross

B – 17, DC, BS, T, AIDS, MD, NS – 23

★ It is hoped to set up a home-care team in November 1989. The 17-bed unit cares for AIDS patients only (there are also 12 beds for young severely handicapped people).

St Joseph's Hospice
Mare Street
Hackney
London E8 4SA
Tel. 01 985 0861

Location: 1 mile north of Bethnal Green underground station
Catchment: unlimited, but generally London and Home Counties
Contacts: Sister Superior/Matron – Sister Helen Cunningham
Medical Director – Dr John Wiles
Administrator – Mr John Scott
Home-care contact: The Secretary – 01 986 6422

B – 108, HC, DC, OT/PT, BS, T, AIDS,* MND/OTI, MD, NS – 134

* Only where AIDS is cancer related – facilities for AIDS patients at nearby Mildmay Mission.

The Margaret Centre
Whipps Cross Hospital
Leytonstone E11 1NR
Tel. 01 556 0821

Contacts: Medical Director – Dr Richard Beaver
Nursing Officer – Miss Vivienne Hancock
Social Worker – Ms Susan Blake

B – 12, HC, DC, MND, AIDS, HST, BS, MD, NS – 21 WTE

LONDON, EAST-CENTRAL

Support Care Team
St Bartholomews Hospital
West Smithfield
London EC1A 7BE
Tel. 01 601 8888

Location: closest underground stations are Farringdon and St Pauls
Catchment: referrals from within St Bartholomews Hospital
Contacts: Lecturer in Care of the Dying – Dr A.T. Tate
Head of Nursing Services – Miss J. Hockley
Home-care contact: 01 601 8500

HST, HC, T, AIDS, MND/OTI, NS – 3

★ This team is hoping to expand into a Department of Palliative Medicine but no date is yet known.

LONDON, NORTH

Macmillan Support Service
Lordship Lane Clinic
239 Lordship Lane
Tottenham
London N17 6AA
Tel. 01 801 6021

Location: ½ mile from Tottenham High Road
Catchment: London Borough of Haringey
Contact: Co-ordinator of Terminal Care – Mrs B. Southam

HC, BS, AIDS, MND/OTI, NS – 4

The North London Hospice
269 Ballards Lane
Finchley
London N12 8NR
Tel. 01 446 6572

Location: Ballards Lane runs between Finchley Central and North Finchley
Catchment: Health Authority of Barnet & Haringey (& Enfield in future)
Contact: Administrator – Penni Montgomery
Home-care contact: Sister Harriet Copperman

HC, BS, T, AIDS, MND/OTI, NS – 4

★ There are plans to open an in-patient unit in 1991, as well as a day hospice. Please note this hospice is inter-faith and non-sectarian. They are concerned to cater for the needs of people of all faiths and those of no formal faith.

Community Liaison Sisters
North Middlesex Hospital
Edmonton
London N18 1QX
Tel. 01 807 3071, ext 2809

★ Referrals from hospital only.

Continuing Care Support Team
Ridge House Clinic
Church Street
Edmonton
London N9
Tel. 01 364 1179

HC, MND, AIDS

Islington Support Team
Archway Wing (Ground Floor)
Whittington Hospital
London N19 5NF
Tel. 01 272 3070, ext 4228
(24 hr answerphone)

Location: ½ mile north from Archway
    underground station on Highgate
    Hill
Catchment: Islington Health Authority
Contacts: Team Leader – Jackie
    Saunders
Palliative Care Consultant – Anna
    Kuroska

HST, HC, BS, AIDS, MND/OTI, NS – 4

LONDON, NORTH-WEST

Edenhall Marie Curie Home
11 Lyndhurst Gardens
Hampstead
London NW3 5NS
Tel. 01 794 0066

Location: close to Haverstock Hill in
    Hampstead, nearest underground
    station Belsize Park
Contacts: Matron/Manager – Miss A.
    Barnard
Consultant in Palliative Care – Dr
    A.T. Tookman

B – 37, DC, OT/PT, BS, T, AIDS,* MD, NS – 53

* AIDS patients accepted if they have cancer.

Bloomsbury Community Care Team
National Temperance Hospital
Hampstead Road
London NW1 2LT
Tel. 01 380 9760

Location: within 5 minutes' walking
    distance of Euston Station

Catchment: all patients with HIV-related
    problems within Bloomsbury Health
    Authority, patients of the Middlesex
    and University College Hospitals
    wherever they live
Contacts: Consultant – Dr Rob George
    Administrator – Miss C. Dobney
Clinical Nurse Specialists – Miss V.
    Robinson & Miss G. Howes
Social Worker – Miss C. Betteridge
Research Assistant – Miss L. Butters

HST, HC, BS, T, AIDS, NS – 2

Bloomsbury Support Team
National Temperance Hospital
Hampstead Road
London NW1 2LT
Tel. 01 387 9300, ext 5358 (UCH
    switch), 0608/9726 direct lines

Location: central London
Catchment: Bloomsbury Health
    Authority
Contacts: Team Administrator – Joyce
    Bell
Team Doctor – Dr Bill O'Neill
Sisters – Jill Highet and Myfanwy
    James (& Margaret Vincent p/t)
Social Worker – Julia Franklin
Research Fellow – Dr Irene Higginson

HST, HC, BS, T, NS – 2.5

Palliative Care/Support Team
Radiotherapy Department
Royal Free Hospital
Pond Street
London NW3
Tel. 01 794 0500, ext 3861

Location: North London
Catchment: Hampstead Health District
Contacts: Consultant in Palliative Care –
    Dr A.T. Tookman
Director of Nursing Services – Mrs
    Maureen Eley
Home-care contact: Team Administrator
    – Mrs Murrell – 794 0500, ext 3861

HST, HC, BS, T, AIDS, MND/OTI, NS – 4

Catherine McAuley Unit
Hospital of St John & St Elizabeth
60 Grove End Road
London NW8 9NH
Tel. 01 286 5126

Location: west of St John's Wood
    underground station (2 min. walk)

Catchment: none for in-patients
Home-care – Bloomsbury Health
    Authority, London Borough of
    Westminster & within 3 miles.
Contact: Medical Director – Dr Philip
    Jones
Home-care contact: Secretary – 286
    5126, ext 330

B – 10, HC, BS, T, AIDS, MND/OTI, MD, NS – 13

★ A day hospice will be opening in 1991.

LONDON, SOUTH-EAST

Greenwich Macmillan Support Team
394 Shooters Hill Road
London SE18 4LP
Tel. 01 319 1991

Location: next door to Brook Hospital,
    on A207
Catchment: London Borough of
    Greenwich/Greenwich Health
    Authority
Contact: Nurse Manager – Mrs Anne
    Sullivan
Home-care contact: 01 319 1991

HST, HC, OT/PT, BS, AIDS, MND NS – 4

★ A day hospice is planned for the
future.

Guy's Support Team
Doyles House
Guy's Hospital
St Thomas Street
London SE1 9RT
Tel. 01 378 1880 (direct), 955 5000
    (hospital)

Location: 500 yards from London Bridge
    Station
Catchment: North Southwark
Contact: Dr Clare Terrell

HST, HC, AIDS, MD, NS – 3

Macmillan Support Team (Lewisham)
Hither Green Hospital
Hither Green Lane
London SE13 6RU
Tel. 01 698 4618 (direct), 4311, ext
    8120 (hospital)

Location: on site of Hither Green
    Hospital, 10 mins walk from Hither
    Green station
Contact: Dr Clare Terrell

HST, HC, O/T, BS, AIDS,* MD, NS – 2

* AIDS patients will be accepted when a special AIDS
nurse is appointed in late 1989/early 1990. There is also
the possibility of taking patients with MND and other
terminal illnesses in the future if the number of nurses
can be increased.

The Pain Relief Unit
King's College Hospital
Denmark Hill
Camberwell
London SE5 9RS
Tel. 01 274 6222, bleep 181

Contacts: Consultant in charge – Dr
    Magdi Hanna
    Senior Nurse – Jane Latham

HST

★ Referrals from consultants and GPs re.
hospital in-patients only.

St Christopher's Hospice
51–9 Lawrie Park Road
Sydenham
London SE26 6DZ
Tel. 01 778 9252

Location: near the South Circular, on the
    Crystal Palace Hill
Catchment: south-east London, Bromley
    & Croydon
Contacts: Chairman –Dame Cicely
    Saunders
    Medical Director – Dr T. West
    Matron – Mrs B. Saunders
    Administrator – Mr C. Clark
    Director of Studies – Dr A. Smith
Home-care contact: Home Care Director
    – 01 778 9252

B – 62, HC, DC, OT/PT, BS, T, AIDS, MND, MD,
NS – 115

Camberwell Macmillan Continuing
    Care Team
St Giles Hospital
St Giles Road
Camberwell
London SE5 7RN
Tel. 01 703 6526

Location: left off Camberwell Church
    Street which links Camberwell &
    Peckham
Catchment: Camberwell Health
    Authority

Contacts: Medical Director – Dr Keith
Pettingale
Senior Nurse – Miss Patricia Wallace
Home-care contact: Secretary – 01 703
6526 (referral by doctors only)

HC, DC, BS, AIDS, MND/OTI, MD, NS – 3

★ The home-care service is already in
operation but day care will not start until
spring 1990. As from April 1990 this
service will be moving to Macmillan
Green, 475 Lordship Lane, East
Dulwich, London SE22.

The Support Team of St Thomas's
Hospital
The Richard Dimbleby Day Centre
Lambeth Wing
St Thomas's Hospital
London SE1 7EH
Tel. 01 928 9292, ext 3648 (main
office), ext 3109 (Senior Registrar),
ext 2876 (in-patient nurses), ext 3
(community sisters)

Location: south of the river Thames on
the west side of Westminster Bridge
Catchment: St Thomas's Hospital, South
Western Hospital, Lambeth
Community Care Centre & West
Lambeth Health district
Contacts: St Thomas's Senior Nurse –
Sister Janie Grant
Community – West Lambeth Health
Authority – Sister Catherine
Lewington
Research Fellow – Dr Rosemary
Lennard
Secretary – Miss Fiona Wilson
Medical Director – Dr Thelma Bates
Home-care contact: Senior Nurse
(Community) – Sister Catherine
Lewington

HST, HC, DC, OT/PT, BS, T, AIDS, MD, NS – 5

LONDON, SOUTH-WEST

Brompton Hospital Support Team
Fulham Road
Chelsea
London SW3 6HP
Tel. 01 352 8121 or bleep

Contacts: Clinical Nurse Specialist –
Wendy Burford
Social Worker – Christine Toone

B – 6, HST, AIDS

★ For patients with lung cancer and
respiratory problems only. Referrals
from within Brompton Hospital only.

The Continuing Care Unit
The Royal Marsden Hospital
Fulham Road
London SW3 6JJ
Tel. 01 352 8171

Contacts: Consultant Physician – Dr
Geoffrey Hanks
Senior Nurse – Catherine Miller

B – 13, HC, AIDS, T

★ Referrals from within hospital only.

The Support Team
The Oncology Unit
St George's Hospital
Blackshaw Road
Tooting
London SW17 0QT
Tel. 01 672 1255

Contacts: Medical Adviser – Dr Charles
Coombes
Home-Care Sister – Gillian Hutchison

★ Referrals from hospital only.

Trinity Hospice
30 Clapham Common North Side
London SW4 0RN
Tel. 01 622 9481

Location: on north side of Clapham
common within ¼ mile of South
Circular
Catchment: North-West Thames –
Hounslow, Riverside, South-West
Thames – Merton & Sutton,
Richmond, Twickenham,
Wandsworth, South-East Thames –
West Lambeth
Contacts: Director & Consultant
Physician – Dr J. Chamberlain
Director of Nursing Services – Miss
M. Marks
Administrator – Mr A.S. Wills
Director of Appeals – Mr D.A.
Ireland
Home-care contact: Ms Jenny Baynham
– 01 622 9481

B – 30, HC, DC, OT/PT, BS, T, AIDS,* MND, MD,
NS – 52 WTE

* Home care provided for AIDS patients but in-patient
facilities provided elsewhere in locality.

Westminster Hospital
Oncology Nursing Area
Dean Ryle Street
London SW1P 2AP
Tel. 01 828 9811

Location: off Horseferry Road, opposite
    Lambeth Bridge
Catchment: south of England
Contact: Senior Nurse – Andrew Knight
Home-care contacts: Jane Richardson,
    Mirella James – 01 400 9666

HC, HST, BS, AIDS, MD, NS – 2

LONDON, WEST

Macmillan Support Team
Parson's House
Charing Cross Hospital
Fulham Palace Road
London W6 8RF
Tel. 01 846 6136

Contacts: Sisters – Ruth Bedford, Sally
    Bradford

HST, HC

★ Referrals from hospital and
community in Hammersmith/
Fulham/Chiswick

The Symptom Care Team
Department of Haematology &
    Oncology
Hospital for Sick Children
Great Ormond Street
London WC1 3JH
Tel. 01 405 9200, ext 5383

Contacts: Medical Director – Dr Ann
    Goldman
    Nursing Sisters – Sharon Beardsmore,
    Jane Hunt

HST

★ Referrals from hospital and home care.

London Lighthouse
111–7 Lancaster Road
London W11 1QT
Tel. 01 792 1200

Location: west of Ladbroke Grove,
    North Kensington
Catchment: London-based for
    community services. Residential
    services, counselling and training
    have no catchment area.
Contacts: Director – Christopher Spence
    Finance & Administration Manager –
    Una O'Brien
    Communications and Fund-raising
    Manager – Mary Pipes
    Central Services Manager – Jane
    Mellor
    Acting Community Services Manager
    – Cliff Swann

Counselling and Training Manager –
    Stephanie Malach
    Residential Services Manager –
    Hamish MacGregor
    Principal Medical Officer – Dr Simon
    Mansfield
Home-care contact: Community Services
    Department – 01 792 1200

B – 24, HC, OT/PT, BS, T, AIDS, MD, NS – 38

★ London Lighthouse offers a wide range
of services to people with HIV, ARC and
AIDS.

The Cancer Counsellors
The Middlesex Hospital
Radiotherapy Department
Mortimer Street
London W1N 8AA
Tel. 01 636 8333, ext 4407

Contacts: Senior Nurses – Teresa Curtis,
    Susan Kibler

★ Supportive/advisory service for cancer
patients at any stage of their illness.

Referrals from within Middlesex Hospital
only.

Pembridge Continuing Care Unit
Paddington Community Hospital
7a Woodfield Road
London W9 2BB
Tel. 01 286 6669

Location: off Harrow road near
    Westbourne Park underground
    station
Catchment: Parkside Health Authority &
    Riverside West. Northern part of
    Riverside East & Bloomsbury. Will
    consider Chiswick
Contacts: Consultant – Dr Anne
    Naysmith
    Senior Nurse – Jane Billington
    Social Worker – Sue Harrison
Home-care contact: Pam Meredith –
    01 286 6669, ext 240

B – 17, HC, BS, MD, NS – 33

The Cancer Counsellor
*The Royal National Throat, Nose &
    Ear Hospital*
Gray's Inn Road
London WC1X 8DA
Tel. 01 837 8855, ext 4127

Catchment: all hospitals in Bloomsbury
within 1 mile of King's Cross, Euston
or Tottenham Court Road stations
Contact: Cancer Counsellor – Linda
Masters

BS. T

★ Advice on symptom control, resource
liaison.

Macmillan Service
University College Hospital
Gower Street
London WC1E 6AU
Tel. 01 387 9300

LOUGHBOROUGH,
LEICESTERSHIRE

Macmillan Service
Loughborough Health Centre
Pinfold Gate
Loughborough
LE11 1DQ
Tel. 0509 611600, ext 8420

Location: in town centre behind
Loughborough General Hospital
Catchment: Loughborough/Charnwood
Contacts: Macmillan nurse – Miss W.M.
Sargeant
Assistant Service Manager – District
Nursing – Mrs J.E. Hard

HC. BS. C. AIDS. NS – 1

LUTON, BEDFORDSHIRE

The Symptom Control Team
Luton and Dunstable Hospital
Lewsey Road
Luton
LU4 ODZ
Tel. 0582 491 122, bleep 139

Contacts: Medical Adviser – Dr David
Siegler
Nursing Officer – Sally Tebbutt

HST

Macmillan Service
Marsh Farm Health Clinic
Purley Centre
The Moakes
Marsh Farm
Luton
LU3 3SR
Tel. 0582 573564

HC

LYMINGTON, HAMPSHIRE

Macmillan Service
Milford Hospital
Sea Road
Milford on Sea
Lymington
Tel. 0590 44878

MACCLESFIELD, CHESHIRE

The East Cheshire Hospice
Millbank Drive
Macclesfield
SK10 3DR
Tel. 0625 610364

Location: on outskirts of the town in
Upton, 1¼ miles from town centre
Catchment: Macclesfield Health
Authority
Contact: Matron – Miss Ann Currington
Home-care contact: Head of Community
Nursing – Mrs I. Scholes – 0625
21000

B – 10/12. HC, DC, OT/PT. BS, AIDS, MND/OTI,
MD, NS – 17.5 WTE

MAIDSTONE, KENT

Maidstone Hospice
Preston Hall
Maidstone
ME20 7NJ
Tel. 0622 747255

Location: 3 miles north-west of town
centre
Catchment: Maidstone Health Authority
Contact: H.V.D. Hallett, Administrator,
Maidstone Hospice Appeal, c/o
Linton Hospital, Coxheath,
Maidstone, ME17 4AH
Tel. 0622 747255
Home-care contact: Mrs Lyn Lane –
0622 710161

B – 10, HC, DC. OT/PT. BS, MND/OTI, MD

★ This is a *project*, due to open in
January 1990.

Macmillan Service
Farm Cottage
Maidstone Hospital
Hermitage Lane
Maidstone
ME16 9QQ
Tel. 0622 26381

Location: on Maidstone Hospital site,
2 miles south of A20 junction with
M20
Catchment: Maidstone Health Authority
Contacts: Nurse Manager – L.K. Lane
Senior Nurse – L. Shevlin
Home-care contact: via patient's GP or
phone 0622 26381

HC, AIDS, NS – 2

MANCHESTER, CHESHIRE

Macmillan Service
Hulme Combined Clinic
217 Hulme Walk
Royce Road
Manchester
M15 5FQ
Tel. 061 226 5211

Location: 1 mile from Manchester Royal
Infirmary (off A5203)
Catchment: Central Manchester
Contact: Primary Care Services Manager
– Miss M. Senior, Derbyshire
House, 293a Upper Brook Street,
Manchester 13

HC, BS, AIDS, NS – 2

MANSFIELD, NOTTINGHAMSHIRE

Macmillan Service
Oak Tree Lane Health Centre
Jubilee Way South
Mansfield
Tel. 0623 651261

HC

MARKET HARBOROUGH, LEICESTERSHIRE

Macmillan Service
The Cottage Hospital
Coventry Road
Market Harborough
LE16 9DD
Tel. 0858 410500

HC

MARLOW, BUCKINGHAMSHIRE

Wycombe Macmillan Service
Marlow Hospital
Glade Road
Marlow
SL7 1DJ
Tel. 06284 72537

Catchment: Wycombe Health Authority
Contact: Matron/Manager – Marlow
Hospital

HC, T, AIDS, MND/OTI, NS – 4

MELROSE, BORDERS

Macmillan Palliative Care Service
Room 1.A.W.2.
Borders General Hospital
Melrose
TD6 9BS
Tel. 0896 4333, ext 1002

Location: ¼ mile south of Melrose on
A6091
Catchment: Scottish Borders Region
Contacts: Medical Consultant – Dr
Shirley Douglas
Macmillan Nursing Sisters – Patricia
McMahon, Christine Gray
Secretary – Margaret Tough

HST, HC, T, AIDS, MND/OTI, MD, NS – 2

MELTON MOWBRAY, LEICESTERSHIRE

Macmillan Service
War Memorial Hospital
Ankle Hill
Melton Mowbray
Tel. 0664 67891

HC

MEOPHAM, KENT

Lions Hospice Ltd
c/o 'The Homestead'
Meopham Green
DA13 0PZ
Tel. 0474 568347

Location: expected to be 2 miles south
of Gravesend town centre, adjacent
to A2
Catchment: Dartford & Gravesham
Health Authority
Contact: Chairman, address as above

★ This is a *project* which hopes eventually
to offer 10 beds and day care.

MERTHYR TYDFIL,
GLAMORGAN

Macmillan Service
The Hollies Health Centre
Swan Street
Merthyr Tydfil
Tel. 0685 4023

HC

Macmillan Service
St Tydfil's Hospital
Merthyr Tydfil
CF47 OSJ
Tel. 0685 723244

MIDDLESBROUGH,
CLEVELAND

Teesside Hospice Care Foundation
10a Cambridge Road
Middlesbrough
TS5 5NQ
Tel. 0642 816777

Location: 2 miles from town centre, off
A1032
Catchment: north and south Tees Health
Authority
Contacts: Administrator – Cedric
Tideswell
Macmillan Team Leader – Sandra
Young
Home-care contact: Sandra Young –
0642 816777

HC, DC, OT/PT, BS, T, AIDS, MND/OTI

★ Three Macmillan teams cover this area
– based at Middlesbrough, Guisborough
and Stockton-on-Tees. There are plans
for an in-patient unit with 8 beds.

MIDHURST, WEST SUSSEX

West Sussex Macmillan Service
Midhurst
GU29 OBL
Tel. 0730 812341

Location: 3 miles north of Midhurst, off
A286
Catchment: Chichester Health Authority
and beyond, to include Petersfield,
Bordon, Liphook, Hindhead,
Godalming, Billingshurst,
Storrington
Contacts: Medical Director – Dr M.A.
McKenna
Senior Nurse – Miss E.A.C. Pelmore
Principal Social Worker – Mr S.
Everard

Voluntary Services Organizer – Mrs
R. Morris
Office Manager – Mrs J. O'Brien
Registered Tutor – Mrs F.M. Fowler
Home-care contact: Dr McKenna –
0730 812341

B – 12, HC, BS, T, C, AIDS, MD, NS – 25

MILTON,
CAMBRIDGESHIRE

*Cambridge Children's Hospice Trust
for East Anglia*
Milton
Cambridge
CB4 4AB
Tel. 0223 860306

Location: 5 miles north of Cambridge city
centre on A45/A10
Catchment: the Eastern region –
Norfolk, Suffolk, Lincolnshire,
Bedfordshire, Hertfordshire, Essex,
Cambridgeshire
Contacts: Matron – Miss Sue Potter
Chairman of Trustees – Canon Fred
Kilner

B – 12, BS, T, AIDS, MND/OTI, NS – 10 trained +
10 auxiliaries

MILTON KEYNES,
BUCKINGHAMSHIRE

The Hospice of our Lady & St John
Manor Farm
Willen Village
Milton Keynes
MK15 9AB
Tel. 0908 663636

Location: 2 miles south of Newport
Pagnell
Catchment: Milton Keynes, part of
Aylesbury Vale and part of South
Bedfordshire
Contact: Sister in Charge
Home-care contact: 0908 663636

B – 10, HC, DC, OT/PT, BS, NS – 13.5

MOGGERHANGER,
BEDFORDSHIRE

Sue Ryder Home
St John's
Moggerhanger
Bedford
MK44 3RJ
Tel. 0767 40622

Location: between Bedford and Sandy on
A603

Catchment: North & South Bedfordshire,
Hertfordshire – but will consider
anywhere
Contacts: Director of Patient Care – Mr
M. Cracknell
Medical Director – Mr R. Peatfield
Home-care contact: Home Care Sister –
0767 40893

B – 20, HC, BS, T, MD, NS – 26 WTE

MONMOUTH, GWENT

Monmouth General Hospital
15 Hereford Road
Monmouth
NP5 3HP
Tel. 0600 35223

MiniMac – 2 beds

MOUNTAIN ASH, GLAMORGAN

Macmillan Service
Community Offices
Mountain Ash General Hospital
Mountain Ash
CF45 4DE
Tel. 0685 872411

HC

NEWBURY, BERKSHIRE

The Newbury and District Cancer Care
Trust
Trust Co-ordinator
Newbury and District Hospital
Andover Road
Newbury
Tel. 0635 31542

Catchment: West Berkshire Health
Authority
Contact: Cancer Care Trust – 0635 31542
Home-care contact: Macmillan nurses –
0635 69666

B – 2, BS, T, C, AIDS

★ Volunteer group providing support,
sitting and loans service. Home care via
local Macmillan nurses. Day-care
facilities to be provided late 1989/early
1990.

Macmillan Service
Thatcham Health Centre
Bath Road
Thatcham
Newbury
Tel. 0635 67171

Contacts: Macmillan nurses – Mrs
Elizabeth Smith, Mrs Claire Soper

HC

NEWBURY, READING & WOKINGHAM

West Berkshire Cancer Care Project
West Berkshire Health Authority

Contact: General Manager, Community
Services Unit – Mr A.J. Hampshire
– 0734 862277

★ Planning day care at Newbury and
Wokingham – to open early 1990.
Planning in-patient unit and day care at
Reading later.

NEWCASTLE UPON TYNE, TYNE & WEAR

Conrad House Marie Curie Home
Bentinck Terrace
Newcastle upon Tyne
NE4 6US
Tel. 091 273 7931/2

Location: close to Newcastle General
Hospital on the A69 to Hexham
Contact: Matron/Manager – Mr G.R.
Lowson

B – 38, DC, OT/PT, BS, T, AIDS*, MD, NS – 28

* AIDS patients accepted if they have cancer.

Macmillan Nurse Support Team
Regional Radiotherapy Centre
Newcastle General Hospital
Westgate Road
Newcastle upon Tyne
NE4 6BE
Tel. 091 273 8811

Location: 1½ miles from town centre on
Newcastle to Carlisle road, A6115 –
turning into A69
Catchment: Newcastle General Hospital
Contact: Nurse Manager – Mrs M.
Bellerby

HST, BS, AIDS, MND/OTI, NS – 2

St Oswald's Hospice
Regent Avenue
Gosforth
Newcastle upon Tyne
NE3 1EE
Tel. 091 285 0063

Location: 2 miles north of Newcastle on
A6127 adjacent to Regent Centre

(300 metres from Regent Centre
Metro Station)
Catchment: mainly 15-mile radius of
Hospice but all referrals within
Northern Region Health Authority
accepted
Contacts: Director of Administration –
Geoffrey S.N. Dorin
Medical Director – Claud F.B.
Regnard
Matron – Anne F. Ruddick-Bracken
Home-care contact: 091 285 0063

B – 20. HC. DC. OT/PT. BS. T. C. AIDS. MND/OTI.
MD. NS – 24

NEWMAINS, STRATHCLYDE

Macmillan Service
Newmains Health Centre
14 Manse Road
Newmains
ML2 9AY
Tel. 0698 381006

Location: 200 yards from A71 at
Newmains roundabout
Catchment: Motherwell/Clydesdale
Contacts: Macmillan nurses – Mrs
Margaret Sturgeon, Miss Marie
Purcell

HC. BS. NS – 2

NEWPORT, GWENT

St David's Foundation
Cambrian House
St John's Road
Newport
NP9 8GR
Tel. 0633 281811/270980

Location: 1 mile east of town centre on
A48
Contacts: Administrator – Mr Karl Gale
Director of Nursing – Miss Heulwen
Egerton
Medical Director – Dr G. Anderson
(advisory capacity only)
Home-care contact: Nursing Service –
0633 270980/281811

HC. DC. BS. T. AIDS. MND/OTI. MD. NS – 14 f/t +
night nursing 'bank'

NEWPORT, ISLE OF WIGHT

Earl Mountbatten House
Fairlee Hospital
Newport
Isle of Wight
PO30 3ES
Tel. 0983 529511/522106

Contacts: Sister/Manager – Mrs A.
Jewitt
Medical Director – Dr N. Coles

B – 10. HC. DC. OT/PT. BS. T. MD. NS – 25

NORTHAMPTON, NORTHAMPTONSHIRE

Cynthia Spencer House
Manfield Hospital
Northampton
NN3 1AD
Tel. 0604 499516

Location: 2 miles north-east of town
centre on A43
Catchment: Northamptonshire
Contacts: Medical Director – Dr Peter
Kaye
Senior Clinical Nurse – Mrs Jackie
Phillips
Home-care contact: Belinda Gibbes
(secretary) – 0604 491121, ext 3223

B – 20. HC. DC. OT/PT. BS. T. AIDS. MND. MD.
NS – 27.13 WTE

NORTHWOOD, MIDDLESEX

Michael Sobell House
Mount Vernon Hospital
Northwood
HA6 2RN
Tel. 09274 26111, ext 4302/4531

Location: Metropolitan Line (Watford
train). Buses from Northwood,
Ruislip, Eastcote and Uxbridge
Catchment: North-West Thames Region
Contacts: Head of Service – Mrs Beryl
Howard
Consultant Physician – Dr Ivan
Trotman
Secretary – Mrs Gloria Webb
Social Worker – Mrs Sue Tippen
Home-care contact: Liz Luck (ext 4652),
Janet Conabeer (ext 4648), Audrey
Foulkes (ext 4647)

B – 18. HC. DC. OT/PT. BS. T. AIDS. MND/OTI.
NS – 30.93 WTE

NORWICH, NORFOLK

Priscilla Bacon Lodge
Macmillan Continuing Care Unit
Colman Hospital
Unthank Road
Norwich
Tel. 0603 628377, ext 714

Contacts: Medical Director – Dr J. Blyth
Nursing Officer – Mrs M. Hughes

Administrator – Mrs B. Shackcloth
Social Worker – Mrs Hilary Bolger

B – 25, HC, BS, DC, MND, T, MD

NOTTINGHAM, NOTTINGHAMSHIRE

Macmillan Continuing Care Unit
Hayward House
City Hospital
Hucknall Road
Nottingham
NG5 1PB
Tel. 0602 691169, ext 2870

Contact: Medical director – Dr Ray
Corcoran

B – 25, HC, DC, MND, T, MD

The Nottinghamshire Hospice
384 Woodborough Road
Nottingham
NG3 4JF
Tel. 0602 606265

Location: 1 mile from the centre of
Nottingham
Catchment: 10-mile radius of the Hospice
Contacts: Senior Nurse Manager – Mrs
P.A. Ritchie
Administrative Assistant – Mrs J.
Dalton
Home-care contact: Mrs P.A. Ritchie
– 0602 606265

HC, DC, OT/PT, BS, T, AIDS, MND/OTI, MD,
NS – 4

NUNEATON, WARWICKSHIRE

Macmillan Service
George Eliot Hospital
College Street
Nuneaton
CV10 7QX
Tel. 0203 384201

★ Referrals from hospital and
community.

Mary Ann Evans Unit
George Eliot Hospital
College Street
Nuneaton
CV10 7QX
Tel. 0203 374797

Contact: Day Care Hospital Manager –
Mrs J. Bates

DC, OT/PT, BS, AIDS, MND

OAKHAM, LEICESTERSHIRE

Macmillan Service
Rutland Memorial Hospital
Cold Overton Road
Oakham
LE15 6NT
Tel. 0572 2552

HC

OLD COLWYN, CLWYD

Macmillan Service
Colwyn Bay Community Hospital
Hesketh Road
Old Colwyn
Tel. 0492 515218

HC, BS

OLDHAM, CHESHIRE

Dr Kershaw's Hospice
Turf Lane
Royton
Oldham
Tel. 061 624 2727

Contacts: Medical Director/Chairman –
Mr Naru Hira
Nursing Co-ordinator – Miss Mary
Hope

HC, DC, MD

Macmillan Service
St Peter's House
St Peter's Precinct
Oldham
OL1 1JT
Tel. 061 624 0544

ORMSKIRK, LANCASHIRE

Macmillan Service
Ormskirk & District General Hospital
Ormskirk
L39 2AZ
Tel. 0695 75471

Hettinga House
St Joseph's Hospice Association
Dark Lane
Ormskirk
Tel. 0695 72942

Contacts: Medical Officer – Dr M.
Cleary
Matron – Miss M. Woods
Administrator – Mr J. Allen

B – 18, MND

ORPINGTON, KENT

South Bromley Hospiscare
Orpington Hospital
Sevenoaks Road
Orpington
BR6 9JU
Tel. 0689 29010/20027

Location: 1 mile south of Orpington town
centre
Catchment: Hospital Support – Bromley,
Farnborough & Orpington Hospitals
Home-Support Team – Bromley
Common & Chislehurst, St Paul's
and St Mary Cray, Biggin Hill,
Farnborough, Orpington
Contacts: Medical Director – Dr Beryl
Magrath
Treasurer – Mr R.P. Wilding
Chairman of Trustees – Dr Yvonne
Griffiths
Home-care contact: Medical Secretary –
Mrs Pat Malone – 0689 29010

HST, HC, DC, BS, T, AIDS, MND/OTI, MD, NS – 6

★ Plans to obtain 6 beds, principally for
respite care.

OXFORD, OXFORDSHIRE

Helen House
37 Leopold Street
Oxford
OX4 1QT
Tel. 0865 728251

Location: immediately off the Cowley
Road, 1 mile from Magdalen Bridge
& behind Parish Church of St Mary
& St John
Catchment: Great Britain
Contacts: Founder and Hon. Director –
Mother Frances Dominica
Head Nurse – Mrs Edith Anthem
Administrator – Michael Garside

B – 8, BS, AIDS, MND/OTI, MD, NS – 25

★ This is a hospice for children.

Sir Michael Sobell House
Macmillan Continuing Care Unit
The Churchill Hospital
Headington
Oxford
OX3 7LJ
Tel. 0865 751156

Contacts: Cons. Physician – Dr Michael
Minton
Senior Nurse – Mrs Ann Couldrick

Admin. Secretary – Mrs Joyce
Bostock

B – 20, HC, DC, BS, MND, AIDS, T

PAISLEY, STRATHCLYDE

Accord Hospice
Hospital Grounds
Hawkhead Road
Paisley
PA2 7BL
Tel. 041 889 8169/887 8462

Location: within grounds of Hawkhead
Hospital, 2 miles east of Paisley
Contacts: Chairman and Medical
Director – Dr A. Lawrie Morton
Administrator – Tom Gibson
Home-care contact: Administrator or
Medical Director – 041 889 8169
Macmillan nurses – 041 887 8462

HC, DC, PT/OT, BS, T, MD, NS – 6

PEMBROKE DOCK, DYFED

South Pembrokeshire Hospital
Fort Road
Pembroke Dock
Tel. 0646 682114

MiniMac – 2 beds

PENARTH, GLAMORGAN

Holme Tower Marie Curie Home
Bridgeman Road
Penarth
CF6 2AW
Tel. 0222 700924

Location: down Beach Road to the sea,
second right is Bridgeman Road and
the Home is on the left
Contacts: Matron/Manager – Mrs J.A.
David
Medical Director – Dr I.G. Finlay

B – 38, DC, OT/PT, BS, T, AIDS,* MD, NS – 50

* AIDS patients accepted if they have cancer.

PERTH, TAYSIDE

Macmillan House
Springland
Isla Road
Perth
PH2 7HO
Tel. 0738 39303/39304

Location: 1 mile from town centre on
A93, 'Blairgowrie' bus route
Catchment: 20-mile radius

Contacts: Administrator – Mr M.A.
Haigh, Tayside Health Board. Perth
& Kinross Unit, 113 Leonard Street,
Perth
Director of Nursing Services – Mrs D.
Howat, Drumhar Health Centre,
North Methven Street, Perth
Medical Director – Dr J. Kynaston,
Macmillan House, Perth
Home-care contacts: Director of Nursing
Services – 0738 21181
Social Services – 0738 21191

DC. OT/PT. BS, MD. NS – 4

PETERBOROUGH, CAMBRIDGESHIRE

Macmillan Service
6Y, Room 37
Peterborough District Hospital
Thorpe Road
Peterborough
Tel. 0733 67451

HC

Peterborough Health Authority
41 Priestgate
Peterborough
PE1 1LN
Tel. 0733 51461

Contact: Assistant Director of Planning
– Linda Gale

★ Plans for day-care unit, with in-patient
beds to follow. (Macmillan service
already in area)

PETERLEE, CO. DURHAM

Macmillan Service
Peterlee Child Health Centre
Bede Way
Peterlee
SR8 1AD
Tel. 091 586 2273

HC. BS

PETERSFIELD, HAMPSHIRE

Sue Ryder Home
Bordean House
Langrish
Petersfield
GU32 1EP
Tel. 0730 61005

Contacts: Hon. Cons. in Charge – Dr
P.F. Golding
Matron – Elizabeth Roberts
Administrator – C. Rubra

B – 10 (for cancer patients). BS

PLYMOUTH, DEVON

St Lukes Hospice
Stamford Cottages
Turnchapel
Plymouth
PL9 9XA
Tel. 0752 401172

Location: 6 miles from city centre
Catchment: Plymouth, South Hants, East
Cornwall, Saltash, Torpoint
Contacts: Matron – Mrs Valerie Olliver
Administrative Director – Cmdr
David Crowley

B – 20, HC, DC. OT/PT. BS, T. AIDS.* MND/OTI.
MD. NS – 42

* AIDS-related cancer patients accepted.

PONTEFRACT, WEST YORKSHIRE

Five Towns Plus Hospice Fund Ltd
New Hospice
Halfpenny Lane
Pontefract
Tel. 0977 796470

Location: 1 mile from town centre
Catchment: District Health Authority –
Castleford, Featherstone,
Normanton, Pontefract,
Knottingley, Hemsworth, South
Elmsall
Contacts: Hon. Medical Director – Dr
R.G. Forster
Planning Co-ordinator – Mr M.
Brown
Secretary – Mr G. Tollesson
Home-care contact: Baghill House,
Pontefract – 0977 703291

B – 9. HC. DC. OT/PT. BS, T. C. AIDS. MND/OTI.
MD

★ Hospice is due to open in June/July
1989 but home care already provided.

PONTYPRIDD, GLAMORGAN

Macmillan Service
Pontypridd & District Hospital
The Common
Pontypridd
Tel. 0443 401550

Contact: District Planning Officer – 0443
485122

HC

★ In-patient unit opening 1991.

PORT GLASGOW,
STRATHCLYDE

Macmillan Service
Port Glasgow Health Centre
Bay Street
Port Glasgow
Renfrewshire
Tel. 0475 45321, ext 210

PORTSMOUTH, HAMPSHIRE

Portsmouth Area Hospice Appeal Fund
c/o Councillor John S. Marshall
43 Oakwood Road
Hilsea
Portsmouth
PO2 9QR
Tel. 0705 662931

★ Planning home care and in-patient unit.

PRESTATYN, CLWYD

Macmillan Service
Prestatyn Community Hospital
Prestatyn
LL19 9RD
Tel. 07456 3487

HC

St Kentigern Hospital
Prestatyn Community Hospital
The Avenue
Prestatyn
Clwyd
Tel. 07456 3581

Location: proposed location is Rhyl, to serve North Clwyd
Contact: Appeals Office – 07456 3581

★ This is a *project* which plans to provide 6–8 in-patient beds and a day centre. Date for completion not yet known.

PRESTON, LANCASHIRE

St Catherine's Hospice
Lostock Lane
Lostock Hall
Preston
PR5 5XU
Tel. 0772 37171

Location: 1 mile east of junction 29 – M6, 2 miles east of junction 9 – M61, 3 miles south-east of Preston town centre
Catchment: primarily central Lancashire area of the Preston & Chorley & South Ribble Authorities

Contacts: Matron – Miss E.A. Swarbrick
Administrator – Mr S.A. Sutcliffe
Home-care contacts: Home-care sisters – 0772 451846 (or contact Matron at the Hospice)

B – 12, HC, DC, OT/PT, BS, T, MND/OTI, MD.
NS – 18.4 WTE

RADCLIFFE, MANCHESTER

Hospice for Bury Association
c/o Alan Rowlinson
5 New Road
Radcliffe
Manchester
M26 9LS
Tel. 061 723 5611

★ Building 5-bed unit, working with existing Macmillan home care.

READING, BERKSHIRE

Macmillan Service
Reading and S. Oxon. Community Unit
Dellwood Hospital
Leibenrood Road
Reading
RG3 2DX
Tel. 0734 505276

Catchment: Reading & S. Oxon Community
Contacts: Senior Nurse – Margaret Forbes – 0491 572544
Macmillan nurses – Maggie Davis, Jackie Whitney

HC. C. AIDS. N – 2

REDHILL, SURREY

Macmillan Service
East Surrey Hospital
Three Arch Road
Redhill
RH1 5RH
Tel. 0737 768511

HC and hospital support.

REIGATE, SURREY

The East Surrey Health Authority Symptom Control Team
41 Spring Copse Road
Reigate
Surrey
Tel. 07372 44151

HC – covering Dorking, Caterham, Oxted, Lingfield, Reigate, Redhill.

RHONDDA, GLAMORGAN
Treherbert Hospital
Treherbert
Rhondda
Tel. 0443 771202
MiniMac – 2 beds

RISLEY, DERBY
Draycott Hospice Association
Treetops
Derby Road
Risley
Tel. 0602 391748
Contact: General Secretary – Mrs Cally
Cheetham

★ Converting building for day-care unit
due to open 1990.

ROCHDALE, LANCASHIRE
Macmillan Service
Community Services Unit
Telegraph House
Baillie Street
Rochdale
OL16 1LJ
Tel. 0706 77777
HC

Springhill Hospice
Broad Lane
Rochdale
Tel. 0706 49920

Contacts: Medical Director – Dr R.D.
Gartside
Matron – Mrs Kay Scott
B – 20, DC, MD

ROCHESTER, KENT
Wisdom Hospice
St Williams Way
Rochester
ME1 2NU
Tel. 0634 830456
Location: ½ mile from centre of
Rochester
Catchment: Medway Health Authority
Contacts: Medical Director – Dr David
Oliver
Senior Nurse Manager – Miss Mary
Handy
Social Worker – Mrs Nan McMurray
Home-care contact: Senior Nurse or
Medical Director – 0634 830456

B – 15, HC, DC, OT/PT, BS, AIDS, MND/OTI, MD,
NS – 24.67 WTE

ROMFORD, ESSEX
St Francis Hospice
The Hall
Havering-atte-Bower
Romford
RM4 1QH
Tel. 0708 753319

Location: 4 miles north of Romford
Catchment: Barking, Havering &
Brentwood, Basildon & Thurrock,
eastern part of Redbridge &
southern part of west Essex
Contacts: Administrator – Janet Y.
Emery
Matron – Sue R. Waite
Medical Director – Dr Nia Ellis
Home-care contact: Mrs Jean Walsh –
0708 753319

B – 21, HC, DC, OT/PT, BS, T, MD, NS – 34.2

ROSSENDALE,
LANCASHIRE
Hospice in Rossendale
5 Mayfair Close
Helmshore
Rossendale
BB4 4LL
Tel. 0706 212613 (day), 229854
(evening)

Catchment: Rossendale
Contact: Mrs Dorothy A. Mitchell
Home-care contact: Mrs Eileen Lloyd –
0204 88 4085

HC, DC, OT/PT, BS, T, MND/OTI

★ Volunteer home care already in
operation. Day care to commence
autumn 1989.

ROTHERHAM, SOUTH
YORKSHIRE
Rotherham Hospice Trust
District General Hospital
Moorgate
Rotherham
S60 2UN
Tel. 0709 820000

Contact: Rev. Ralph Weston

★ Planning 10 bed in-patient unit and day
care.

Macmillan Service
Doncaster Gate Hospital
Doncaster Gate
Rotherham
Tel. 0709 820232

Location: centre of town
Contacts: Macmillan nurses – Karen
Jones, Cath Jackson – 0709 820232

HC, BS, AIDS, MND/OTI, NS – 2

**ST ALBANS,
HERTFORDSHIRE**

St Albans and District Hospice Home
Care Team
Hospice Home Care Team
St Albans City Hospital
Normandy Road
St Albans
Tel. 0727 66122

Location: near city centre
Contacts: Chairman – Mr Frank
Kilvington
Nurse Manager – Mrs Zoe Hunt
Medical Director – Dr Mary Groves
Home-care contacts: Nurses, secretary or
answerphone – 0727 66122, ext. 491

HC, DC, PT, BS, T, C, AIDS, MND/OTI, NS – 2 f/t
& 2 p/t

ST AUSTELL, CORNWALL

Mount Edgcumbe Hospice
Porthpean Road
St Austell
PL26 6AB
Tel. 0726 65711/66923

Location: 1 mile out of St Austell,
signposted off town bypass
Catchment: Cornwall and Scilly Isles
Contacts: Matron – Mrs M. West
Medical Director – Dr J. Williams
Bursar – Rev H. Gallichan
Home-care contact: Mrs Valerie Hunkin

B – 18, DC, BS, T, AIDS, MND/OTI, MD, NS – 23
WTE

ST HELENS, MERSEYSIDE

Fairfield House (Nursing Home)
Fairfield Hospital
Crank
St Helens
Merseyside
Tel. 0744 39311

Contacts: Medical Director – Dr John
Higham

Sister in charge – Sister K. Wintle

B – 16 (6 used as hospice beds)

★ Referrals from Macmillan nurses or
hospital consultant, Dr Tappin.

Macmillan Service
Community Nursing Office
St Helen's Hospital
Peasley Cross Wing
Marshalls Cross Road
St Helen's
Tel. 0744 26633, ext 278

HC

**ST LEONARDS-ON-SEA,
EAST SUSSEX**

St Michael's Hospice (Hastings) Ltd
25 Upper Maze Hill
St Leonards-on-Sea
TN38 OLB
Tel. 0424 445177

Location: on A21 ½ mile from sea front
Catchment: Hastings District Health
Authority
Contacts: General Manager – D.F.
Ashton
Matron – Mrs V. Bishop
Medical Director – Dr J. Hocknell

B – 12, DC, OT/PT, BS, T, AIDS, MND/OTI, MD,
NS – 19

ST PETER PORT, GUERNSEY

Hospice Care Sisters
States Board of Health
Community Nursing Department
Lukis House
Grange
St Peter Port
Tel. 0481 25241

HC

SALISBURY, WILTSHIRE

Salisbury Macmillan Unit
Odstock Hospital
Salisbury
SP2 8BJ
Tel. 0722 336262, ext 2113

Location: 1½ miles south of city centre
within grounds of Odstock Hospital
Catchment: Salisbury Health Authority
Contacts: Medical Director – Dr F.J.
Powell
Senior Nurse – Mrs Caroline
Waldman

Hon. Secretary – Mrs Elisabeth Beeley
Social Worker – Ms Jane Daniel
Home-care contacts: Sister Paton, Sister Austing, Sister Manning – 0722 336262, ext 2360 & 2361

B – 6, HC, DC, BS, T, C, AIDS, MND/OTI, MD, NS – 11.5 WTE

SCARBOROUGH, NORTH YORKSHIRE

St Catherine's Hospice
Macmillan House
137 Scalby Road
Scarborough
YO12 6TB
Tel. 0723 351421

Location: 1 mile north of town centre, opposite hospital on main A171
Catchment: to Staithes in the north-east, to Kirbymoorside, Ampleforth, Malton in the west, to Bridlington, Driffield in the south-east
Contacts: Director – Geoff Bishop
Matron – Miss Ruth Ainley
Home-care contact: Matron – 0723 351421

B – 11, HC, DC, OT/PT, BS, T, MND/OTI, MD, NS – 13.4 WTE

SCUNTHORPE, LINCOLNSHIRE

The Support Nurses
Community Health Department
Comforts Avenue
Scunthorpe
Tel. 0724 282282, ext 2741

HC, AIDS

Scunthorpe & District Hospice Appeal (Lindsey Lodge)
Trent House
Hebden Road
Scunthorpe
Tel. 0724 282282

Catchment: Scunthorpe Health Authority
Contacts: Chairman, Hospice Appeal – Mrs A. Tindall
Chairman, Fund Raising Committee – Mrs M. Goodwin
Hon. Secretary – Mrs A. Simpson

Home-care contact: support nurses – 0724 282282, ext 2741

HC

★ The support nurses are already in operation but the day-care unit does not open until 1990. It is hoped that an in-patient unit will also be provided eventually.

SHEFFIELD, SOUTH YORKSHIRE

Macmillan Service
Northern General Hospital
Herries Road
Sheffield 5
Tel. 0742 434343, ext 4940

Location: 2 miles from town centre
Catchment: Northern General Hospital
Contacts: Sister Gahegan, Sister Hibbert

AIDS, MND/OTI, NS – 2

★ Referrals from Northern General Hospital only.

Macmillan Support Nurses
Royal Hallamshire Hospital
Glossop Road
Sheffield
S10 2JF
Tel. 0742 766222/26484

Contacts: Sister B. Hutchcroft, Sister J. Mallinson

★ Support and advisory service within Royal Hallamshire Hospital for patients with cancer and other terminal illness.

St Luke's Hospice
Little Common Lane
Abbey Lane
Sheffield
S11 9NE
Tel. 0742 369911

Contacts: Medical Director – Dr A.G.O. Crowther
Matron – Miss M. Cockburn
Administrator – Mr M. Rapson
Social Worker – Mrs Janet Foster

B – 25, HC, DC, BS, MND, AIDS, T

SHEFFORD,
BEDFORDSHIRE

Macmillan Service
The Health Centre
Iveldale Drive
Shefford
SG17 5AD
Tel. 0462 815262

HC

SHREWSBURY,
SHROPSHIRE

Macmillan Service
Royal Shrewsbury Hospital (South)
Mytton Oak Road
Shrewsbury
SY3 8XF
Tel. 0743 231122, 3294/3863

Location: 1 mile from town centre off the
main A5 road
Catchment: western Shropshire
Contact: Mrs F. Webster

HC, BS, T, AIDS, NS – 3

Shropshire & Mid Wales Hospice
Bilton Heath
Shrewsbury
SY3 8HS
Tel. 0743 236565

Location: on A458, ½ mile from junction
with A5
Catchment: Shropshire and mid Wales
Contacts: Bursar – Mr Peter J. Simpson
Matron – Mrs Margaret Roberts
Medical Director – Dr Jeremy
Johnson

B – 16, DC, OT/PT, BS, MND/OTI, MD

★ An extra 6–9 beds are planned for the
mid 1990s when it is hoped to take AIDS
patients. A home-care service is planned
for 1990–91.

SIDCUP, KENT

Bexley Macmillan Support Team
Queen Mary's Hospital
Sidcup
DA14 6LT
Tel. 01 302 2678, ext 4180/4290

Location: just off A20 and ½ mile south
of town centre
Catchment: London Borough of Bexley
Contact: Senior Macmillan nurse – Mrs
M. Boughton

HC, BS, AIDS, NS – 3

SIDMOUTH, DEVON

Sidmouth, Hospicare
Blackmore Health Centre
Sidmouth
EX10 8ET
Tel. 0395 578706

Location: in centre of town between
public library and local community
hospital
Catchment: the Sidvale area of Sidmouth,
Sidford & Sidbury plus a few
outlying areas.
Contacts: Hospicare Nursing Sister –
Mrs Mary Mackinnon
Chairman Management Committee –
Dr Philip Atkinson
Hon. Secretary Management
Committee – Mrs Eileen Bird
Hon. Treasurer Management
Committee – Mrs Eileen Newby
Home-care contact: Blackmore Health
Centre – 0395 512601

HC, BS, T, MD, NS – 2

SLOUGH, BERKSHIRE

Macmillan Service
The Health Clinic
Burlington Road
Slough
SL1 2JS
Tel. 0753 820833, 0344 572011
(out of hours)

HC, NS – 4

SOLIHULL, WEST
MIDLANDS

Solihull Macmillan Service
Community Health Services
Marston Green Hospital
Berwicks Lane
Marston Green
B37 7XR
Tel. 021 779 6035

Location: Marston Green Hospital, 1½
miles north of NEC/Birmingham
station, 2 miles north of junction 6,
M42 (A45)
Catchment: Solihull District Health
Authority
Contacts: Macmillan nurses – Susan
Harris, Teresa Monteiro – 021 779
6035

HC, BS, T, AIDS, MND/OTI, NS – 2

Warren Pearl Marie Curie Home
911–13 Warwick Road
Solihull
B91 3ER
Tel. 021 705 4607/8

Location: on main Warwick Road, off M42, into city centre
Contact: Matron/Manager – Mrs M.E. Hardware

B – 28, BS, T, AIDS,* MD, NS – 37

* AIDS patients accepted if they have cancer.

SOUTHALL, MIDDLESEX

Meadow House
Ealing Hospital
Uxbridge Road
Southall
UB1 3EU
Tel. 01 574 2444

Location: in grounds of Ealing Hospital
Contact: Senior Nurse, Continuing Care – Mrs M.A. Brennan
Home-care contact: 01 574 2444, ext 2777/2774/2775

B – 14, HC, BS, AIDS, MND/OTI, MD, NS – 25.36

SOUTHAMPTON, HAMPSHIRE

Countess Mountbatten House
Moorgreen Hospital
Botley Road
Southampton
SO3 3JB
Tel. 0703 477414

Location: 1½ miles from junction 7 on the M27 within easy reach of Southampton, Portsmouth & Winchester
Catchment: Southampton, Portsmouth & Winchester
Contacts: Medical Director – Dr Richard Hillier
Nurse Manager – Mrs Rosemary Friend

B – 25, HC, DC, OT/PT, BS, T, MD, NS – 26

SOUTHPORT, LANCASHIRE

Macmillan Service
Health Office
2 Church Street
Southport
PR9 0QU
Tel. 0704 40911

Location: in town centre

HC, NS – 2

Queenscourt
Queenscourt Hospice Office
Southport General Infirmary
Scarisbrick New Road
Southport
PR8 6PH
Tel. 0704 44645

Location: day care provided in hospital premises on promenade; office in town
Catchment: Southport and Formby Health Authority – Southport, Formby, Scarisbrick, Tarleton, Hesketh Bank, Banks
Contact: Secretary – Mrs Pat Williams

HC, DC, OT/PT, BS, MND/OTI, NS – 1

★ At present this group offers day care and a home support/sitting service. They hope to open 10 beds in spring/summer 1990 and to offer further services.

SOUTH SHIELDS, TYNE & WEAR

St Clare's Hospice
3 Westoe Village
South Shields
NE33 3EA
Tel. 90 4567091

Location: 1 mile south of South Shields town centre on A1018 road to Sunderland
Catchment: borough of South Tyneside and District
Contacts: Administrator – Mr James Hayden
Sister in Charge – Mrs Joanne Chinn
Co-ordinator – Mr Reg Redfern
Home-care contacts: Sister Chinn or Nurse Hope – 90 456170

HC, DC, OT/PT, BS, T, AIDS,* MND/OTI, NS – 2

* Will accept AIDS patients for day care and home care if requested.

★ Plans to open 6–7 in-patient beds within the next 5 years.

STAFFORD, STAFFORDSHIRE

Hospice at Home
c/o Mrs V.A. Moore
Stafford District Voluntary Services
Chell Road
Stafford
ST16 2QA
Tel. 0785 45466

HC

★ Plans for day care.

STEVENAGE,
HERTFORDSHIRE

The Lister Hospital
Coreys Mill Lane
Stevenage
SG1 2AB
Tel. 0438 314333, bleep 1390

★ Referrals from hospital only. HC from Hitchin.

STOCKPORT, CHESHIRE

Stockport Terminal Care Team
Heaton Norris Health Centre
Cheviot Close
Heaton Norris
Stockport
SK4 1SX
Tel. 061 480 3647 (nurses), 419 5070 (doctor)

Contact: Cons. Physician – Dr R. Feinmann

HST. HC

STOCKTON-ON-TEES,
CLEVELAND

Butterwick Hospice
96 Bishopton Road
Stockton-on-Tees
TS18 4PA
Tel. 0642 603753/607742

Contacts: Medical Director – Dr I. Kirkbride
Matron – Ms B. Newbegin
Bursar – Mr Robert Jaffray

B – 6, HC, DC, BS, MND

Macmillan Service
Fairfield Clinic
Wellburn Road
Fairfield
Stockton-on-Tees
TS19 7PT
Tel. 0642 585121

HC

STOKE-ON-TRENT,
STAFFORDSHIRE

The Douglas Macmillan Home
Barlaston Road
Blurton
Stoke-on-Trent
ST3 3NZ
Tel. 0782 317118

Location: 3½ miles south-west of the centre of Stoke-on-Trent, between Trentham and Longton on the A5035
Catchment: North Staffordshire, part of Mid Staffordshire and part of South Cheshire
Contact: Chairman – Allan Lucas
Home-care contact: Matron – Mrs P. Booth – 0782 317118

B – 28, HC, DC, BS, T, NS – 50 (mostly p/t)

STONE, STAFFORDSHIRE

Macmillan Service
Trent Hospital
Crown Street
Stone
Tel. 0785 814817

STOURPORT,
WORCESTERSHIRE

Macmillan Service
Stourport Health Centre
Worcester Street
Stourport
Tel. 0299 827131

Catchment: Kidderminster & District Health Authority
Contact: Primary Service Manager – Mrs J. Hinton
Home-care contact: Mrs A. Stephenson – 0299 827131

HC, BS, AIDS, MND/OTI, NS – 2

STREATLEY,
BEDFORDSHIRE

Luton and South Bedfordshire Hospice
Great Bramingham Farm
Bramingham Lane
Streatley
LU3 3NL
Tel. 0582 405090 (9am–5pm, Monday, Tuesday & Wednesday)
(9am–1pm, Thursday & Friday)

Location: on northern boundary of Luton Borough, ½ mile on left of A6 towards Bedford
Catchment: Luton & South Bedfordshire & the immediate areas of Hertfordshire
Contacts: Medical Director – Dr David Siegler
Chairman of Hospice Trust – Dr Winston White
Treasurer – Mr Geoffrey Squires

Appeals Director – Mr Geoffrey Farr
Secretary – Mrs Penny Westley

B – 10, HC, DC, OT/PT, BS, T, MD, NS – 12

★ This is a *project*, planned to open in
1990.

SUNDERLAND, TYNE & WEAR

St Benedict's Hospice
Havelock Hospital
Hylton Road
Sunderland
SR4 8AE
Tel. 091 5656 256, ext 203

Location: 2 miles from town centre
Catchment: between rivers Tyne & Tees
Contacts: Medical Director – Dr Tim
    Lovel
Ward Sister – Margaret Anderson
Social Worker – Mrs Lois Woods
Home-care contact: Sister S. Harrison –
    091 5490960

B – 16, HC, DC, BS, OT/PT, MND, HST, T,
NS – 16

SUNNINGHILL, BERKSHIRE

Community Macmillan Service East
    Berkshire
The Paul Bevan Cancer Foundation
52 High Street
Sunninghill
SL5 9NP
Tel. 0990 24721/21366/28611/23468

Location: Sunninghill High Street, 1 mile
    from Ascot High Street
Catchment: East Berkshire District
Contact: Secretary – Doreen Lancefield

HC, AIDS, NS – 5

SUTTON, SURREY

Continuing Care Unit, Chevalier Ward
Royal Marsden Hospital
Downs Road
Sutton
Tel. 01 642 6011

Location: 1 mile south of Sutton
Contact: Medical Director – Dr Geoff
    Hanks
Home-care contact: Home Care Sister –
    Diane Gibson – 01 642 6011

B – 13, HC, T, AIDS, MND/OTI, MD, NS – 15

SUTTON-IN-ASHFIELD, NOTTINGHAMSHIRE

King's Mill Hospice Trust
King's Mill Hospital Site
Mansfield Road
Sutton-in-Ashfield
Tel. 0623 657866

Location: 1 mile from Mansfield town
    centre on A38 to Sutton-in-Ashfield
Catchment: Central Nottinghamshire
    Health Authority
Contact: Mrs M.F. Lloyd-Mostyn, King's
    Mill Hospice Trust Office, St Peter's
    Chambers, 2a Church Side,
    Mansfield, Notts

★ This is a *project* due to open in autumn
1990 which will offer 12 beds, a day
centre and a home-care service

SWANSEA, GLAMORGAN

Ty-Olwen
Morriston Hospital
Swansea
SA6 6NL
Tel. 0792 703361

Location: 1 mile from junction 46 of M4
Catchment: West Glamorgan
Contacts: Nurse/Patient Services
    Manager – Miss G.M. Cousins
Medical Director – Dr P. Griffiths
Associate Specialist – Dr R. Davies
Home-care contact: Miss G.M. Cousins –
    0792 703361

B – 25, HC, DC, OT/PT, BS, T, MD, NS – 34.76

SWINDON, WILTSHIRE

Prospect Foundation
5 Church Place
Swindon
SN1 5EH
Tel. 0793 616134

Location: offices – facing park off
    Faringdon Road, hospice – in
    Victoria Hospital, Okus Road
Catchment: home care – Swindon
    District
hospice – as above but some patients
    taken from border areas if main
    treatment has been in Swindon
Contacts: Administrator – Robin
    Williams
Senior Nurse Manager – Yvonne
    Roche
P/T Medical Director – Lucinda
    Pritchard

Home-care contact: Nurse Manager or
  sisters – 0793 616134

B – 10, HC, BS, MND, MD, NS – 21 WTE + 'bank'
nurses

★ There are plans to increase the number
of in-patient beds and it may then be
possible to take patients with AIDS and
other terminal illness.

TARRINGTON, HEREFORDSHIRE

Hospice of the Marches
Brookfield
Tarrington
HR1 4HZ
Tel. 0432 79341 (Hereford office), 0242
  525437 (Cheltenham Clinic)

Location: office – on A438 midway
  between Hereford and Ledbury
in-patients in Uplands Nursing Home,
  Church Road, Maisemore, 2 miles
  north of Gloucester on the A417
  from the Over roundabout
Catchment: Herefordshire,
  Gloucestershire, North Gwent
Contacts: Medical Director – Dr Richard
  Lamerton
  Nursing Director – Mrs Patricia
  Lamerton
  Administrator – Mr John Laws
Home-care contact: Dr Lamerton – 0432
  79341

B – 2, HC, DC, BS, T, MND/OTI, MD, NS – 4

TAUNTON, SOMERSET

Symptom Control Team
Musgrove Park Hospital
Taunton
Tel. 0823 333444

Contact: Consultant – Dr Jenny Lovett

★ Hospital referrals only.
3 palliative-care beds available.

St Margaret's Somerset Hospice
Heron Drive
Bishops Hull
Taunton
TA1 5HA
Tel. 0823 259394

Location: 2 miles west of Taunton town
  centre – off A38 to Wellington &
  Exeter
Catchment: Somerset Health Authority
  (excluding the districts of Frome &
  Shepton Mallet seved by Bath
  Health District)

Contacts: Administrator – Mr Chris
  Downing
  Matron – Mrs Sarah Folland
  Medical Director – Dr Jenny Lovett
Home-care contact: Matron – 0823
  259394

B – 16, HC, DC, BS, AIDS, MND, MD, 34.5 WTE

TELFORD, SHROPSHIRE

Macmillan Home Care Nurses
a) *Hadley Health Centre*
Telford
Shropshire
Tel. 0952 53305

HC, NS – 1

b) *Stirchley Health Centre*
Telford
Shropshire
Tel. 0952 53305

HC, BS, NS – 1

TENBY, DYFED

Macmillan Service
Tenby Cottage Hospital
Trafalgar Road
Tenby
Tel. 0834 3111

HC

TIVERTON, DEVON

Tidcombe Hall Marie Curie Home
Tiverton
EX16 4EJ
Tel. 0884 252181

Location: a few hundred yards past
  Blundells School on Blundells Lane
Contact: Matron/Manager – Mrs I.
  Mirams

B – 12, BS, T, AIDS*, MD, NS – 20

*AIDS patients accepted if they have cancer.

★ Beds to increase to 15 in December
1989.

TORQUAY, DEVON

Macmillan Service
Castle Circus Health Service
Abbey Road
Torquay
Tel. 0803 295153

Location: middle of Torquay town centre
Catchment: geographical division of
  Torbay Health Authority

Contact: Team Leader, Macmillan
Service – Mrs B. Bedford

HC, BS, T, NS – 4

Rowcroft House Foundation Ltd
Torbay and South Devon Hospice
Avenue Road
Torquay
Tel. 0803 211656

Location: 1 mile from town centre;
Avenue Road links Newton Road,
main road into Torquay to sea front
Catchment: Torbay Health District
Contacts: Administrator – Mr J.S. Relph
Matron – Miss S. Wimbles
Medical Director – Dr Richard
Scheffer

B – 19, DC, OT/PT, BS, T, AIDS, MND/OTI, MD,
NS – 31 WTE

TRURO, CORNWALL

Macmillan Service
3 St Clement Vean
Tregolls Road
Truro
TR1 1RN
Tel. 0872 77876/40339

Location: 1 mile east of Truro on A390
Catchment: Cornwall
Contacts: Macmillan Nurse Manager –
Mrs Val Hunkin
Administrator – Mrs Alison Gaffney
Home-care contact: Val Hunkin, Alison
Gaffney – 0872 77876/40339

HC, DC, OT/PT, BS, T, AIDS, MND/OTI, NS – 16

TUNBRIDGE WELLS, KENT

*Hospice at Home (The Care
Foundation)*
Michael Tetley Hall
Sandhurst Road
Tunbridge Wells
TN2 3JS
Tel. 0892 544877

Location: off Pembury Road, Tunbridge
Wells
Catchment: Tunbridge Wells Health
Authority
Contacts: Medical Officer –
Nursing Director – Mrs Angela
Walton
Social Work Director – Mrs Helen
Sills
Administrator – Mr David Payne

HC, BS, T, AIDS, MND, NS – 4

ULVERSTON, CUMBRIA

St Mary's Hospice in Furness
Ford Park Crescent
Ulverston
LA12 7JS
Tel. 0229 53072

Contacts: Medical Director – Dr N.
Sawyer
Matron – Mrs Joan Pollitt

B – 6, DC, C, AIDS, MND/OTI, MD, NS – 14

Macmillan Service
Ulverston Health Centre
Victoria Road
Ulverston
LA12 OEW
Tel. 0229 53093

URMSTON, MANCHESTER

Macmillan Service
5 Queens Road
Urmston
Manchester
Tel. 061 748 2214

HC

WAKEFIELD, WEST
YORKSHIRE

Wakefield Hospital Support Team
Pinderfields General Hospital
Aberford Road
Wakefield
WF1 4DG
Tel. 0924 37512, ext 2087

Contacts: GP Medical Adviser – Dr P.
Gajjar
Clinical Nurse Specialist – Mrs Ruth
Brophy
Social Worker – Brian Pearson

HST, BS

Wakefield Hospice
Aberford Road
Wakefield
WF1 4AL
Tel. not yet known

Location: opposite Pinderfields General
Hospital, 1 mile from city centre
Catchment: Wakefield Health Authority
Contacts: Mr Edwin Hirst, Appeal
Manager, Hospice Office, 5 Bank
Street, Wakefield, WF1 1EH. Tel.
0924 361860
Matron – Mrs J. Powell, same address
and tel. no.

Home-care contact: Wakefield
Pinderfields Support Team – 0924
375217

B – 8, HC, DC, OT/PT, BS, MND/OTI, MD, NS – 14

★ This is a *project*, expected to open in
February/March 1990.

WALSALL, WEST MIDLANDS

Macmillan Service
Leckie House
57 Lichfield Street
Walsall
Tel. 0922 720255, ext 221/216

HC

Macmillan Service
Manor Hospital
Moat Road
Walsall
WS2 9PS
Tel. 0922 721172

★ Hospital referrals only.

WAREHAM, DORSET

Macmillan Service
Wareham Health Centre
Stretche Road
Wareham
Tel. 09295 6422

WARRINGTON, CHESHIRE

Macmillan Service
Garven Place Clinic
86 Sankey Street
Warrington
WA1 1RH
Tel. 0925 51188

HC

St Rocco's Hospice
82 Orford Avenue
Orford
Warrington
WA2 7QQ
Tel. 0925 573105

Location: 1 mile from town centre on
A49 north
Catchment: 10-mile radius – Warrington
& Halton Health Districts
Contacts: Medical Director – Dr M.D.
Thomas
Sister in Charge – Mrs C.A. Thomas
Administrator – Mrs G. Hunt
Home-care contact: 0925 51188

B – 9, HC, DC, BS, MND, MD, NS – 10 WTE

WARWICK, WARWICKSHIRE

Macmillan Service
Myton Hamlet Hospice
Myton Lane
Myton Road
Warwick
CV34 6PX
Tel. 0926 492518

Myton Hamlet Hospice
Myton Lane
Myton Road
Warwick
CV34 6PX
Tel. 0926 492518

Location: on A425 between Warwick and
Leamington Spa
Catchment: Warwickshire, including
Coventry
Contacts: Administrator – Mr B.G.
Caley
Matron – Mrs N.L. Walton

B – 24, C, AIDS, MND/OTI, MD, NS – 34 WTE

Macmillan Service
South Warwickshire Hospital
Lakin Road
Warwick
CV34 5BW
Tel. 0926 495321

WELLING, KENT

Greenwich and Bexley Cottage Hospice
91 Bellegrove Road
Welling
Tel. 01 303 6864

Contact: Chairman – Mr Pat Jeavons

★ Planning for an in-patient unit.

WELWYN GARDEN CITY, HERTFORDSHIRE

*Hospice Care Service for East
Hertfordshire*
Isabel Wing
Hall Grove
Welwyn Garden City
AL7 4PH
Tel. 0707 324005

Location: 1 mile east of town centre
Catchment: East Hertfordshire Health
Authority
Contact: Chairman of Trustees – Mr
Harry Overy

Home-care contact: Service Secretary at
    Isabel Wing – 0707 330686

HC, DC, OT/PT, BS, T, AIDS, MND/OTI, MD,
NS – 10

★ There are plans for a 10-bed in-patient
unit to be opened in May 1990.

WEMBLEY, MIDDLESEX

St Luke's Hospice
150 Wembley Hill Road
Wembley
HA9 8EW
Tel. 01 904 3558

Location: ½ mile from Wembley
    Stadium
Catchment: Harrow Health Authority
    plus the Wembley area of Parkside
    Health Authority
Contacts: Chairman – Mr John Corner
    Treasurer – Mr Keith Taylor
    Secretary – Mr Philip J.S. Crome
    Chairman of Medical Committee – Dr
    Elizabeth Milne
Home-care contact: Head of Continuing
    Care, Harrow Hospital – Mrs Irene
    Browne – 01 864 5432

HC, BS, C, AIDS, MND/OTI, NS – 2–3

★ This is a new home-care service with
plans for day care later on.

WESTCLIFF-ON-SEA, ESSEX

Fair Havens
126 Chalkwell Avenue
Westcliff-on-Sea
SS0 8HN
Tel. 0702 344879/431104

Location: near sea front on main road
    leading into Westcliff sea front
Catchment: Southend Health Authority
Contacts: Hon. Medical Director – Dr
    Michael Stuart
    Matron – Mrs Daphne Spencer
    Administrator – Mr Ken Crowe
Home-care contact: 0702 332487

B – 8, HC, DC, OT, BS, T, AIDS, MND/OTI,
MD, NS – 13 WTE

WETHERBY, WEST YORKSHIRE

Martin House
Grove Road
Clifford
Wetherby
LS23 6TX
Tel. 0937 845045

Location: between Boston Spa and
    Clifford – 1 mile to the east of
    the A1
Catchment: no limitation, but mostly
    north of England
Contacts: Head Nurse – Miss Lenore
    Hill
    Administrator – Mr Robin Wood
Home-care contact: 0937 845045

B – 10, HC, DC, OT/PT, BS, T, AIDS, MND/OTI,
MD, NS – 25

★ Martin House offers respite care for
children suffering from terminal disorders
and for their families

WEYBRIDGE, SURREY

Sam Beare Continuing Care service
Weybridge Hospital
Church Street
Weybridge
KT13 8DY
Tel. 0932 852931, ext 29

Location: High Street in town centre
Catchment: North West Surrey Health
    Authority – Weybridge, Byfleet,
    Chertsey, Walton, Woking,
    Addlestone
Contact: Sister Freda Harper
Home-care contact: Sister Dawn Stickney
    – 0932 852931, ext 44

B – 8, HC, BS, T, AIDS, MND, NS – 8

WHITEHAVEN, CUMBRIA

Derwent Ward
West Cumberland Hospital
Whitehaven
CA28 8JG
Tel. 0946 69 3181

Contact: Medical Director – Dr W.T.
    Berrill

B – 5

WIGAN, LANCASHIRE

Wigan Hospice
Poolstock Lane
Wigan
WN3 5HL
Tel. 0942 496092

Location: 1 mile south-west of town
    centre on B5238
Catchment: Wigan District Health
    Authority
Contacts: Matron – Mrs J. Peet
    Medical Director – Dr E. Allen

Administrator – Mrs D. Bradshaw
Acting Sennior Home Care Sister –
Sister J. Spencer
Home-care contact: General Hospice
referral – 0942 496092

B – 12–14, HC, DC, OT/PT, BS, T, AIDS, MND/
OTI, MD, NS – 19.3

WINDSOR, BERKSHIRE

Thames Valley Hospice
Pine Lodge
Hatch Lane
Windsor
SL4 3RW
Tel. 0753 842121

Location: 1 mile from town centre
Catchment: Thames Valley, including
Windsor, Maidenhead, Bracknell,
Slough, High Wycombe
Contacts: Matron – Miss Jennie Lindley
Administrator – Mrs Yvonne
Johnstone

B – 15, DC, OT/PT, AIDS, MND/OTI,
NS – 22.3 WTE

WINSFORD, CHESHIRE

St Luke's (Cheshire) Hospice
Grosvenor House
Queensway
Winsford
CW7 4AW
Tel. 0606 551246

Location: town centre
Catchment: Mid and South Cheshire
Contacts: Administrator – Mr R.
Coombes
Sister in charge – Sister Edith Reeves
Home-care contact: Community Services
Officer – Miss Rose – 0270 626662

DC, OT/PT, C, AIDS, MND/OTI, NS – 4

★ It is proposed to open 10 in-patient
beds but date not yet known.

WIRRAL, MERSEYSIDE

Macmillan Service
Arrowe Park Hospital
Arrowe Park Road
Upton
Wirral
L49 5PE
Tel. 051 678 5111

★ Referrals from within hospital only –
no home visits.

Macmillan Service
Bebington Health Clinic
Civic Way
Bebington
Wirral
Tel. 051 645 7661

HC

Macmillan Service
Pensby Clinic
Pensby Road
Pensby
Wirral
L61 5UB
Tel. 051 648 2212

Location: Wirral Peninsula
Catchment: Metropolitan Borough of
Wirral plus Neston, Burton,
Willaston & Parkgate in the
Borough of Ellesmere Port
Contact: Asst. Director of Nursing
Services – Miss D. White – 051 648
7221
Home-care contact: Macmillan Service –
051 648 2212

HC, BS, AIDS,* NS – 3

* Certain AIDS patients accepted if their symptoms are
mainly those of cancer.

St Johns Hospice in Wirral
Mount Road
Clatterbridge
Bebington
Wirral
L63 6JE
Tel. 051 334 2778

Location: Close to Clatterbridge junction
of M53 motorway
Catchment: The Wirral
Contacts: Administrator – Mr R.R.
Worthington
Matron – Mrs J.O. Jones
Medical Director – Dr J.S. Brock

B – 16, PT, BS, T, AIDS,* MND/OTI,* MD, NS – 26

* The prime reason for admission is painful terminal
illness. If this applies, then patients with AIDS, MND
or other terminal illness would be admitted.

WISBECH, CAMBRIDGESHIRE

Fenland Hospice and Day Hospice
Fenland Hospice Office
Queen's Road
Wisbech
PE13 2AB
Tel. 0945 65778

Location: ¼ mile from town centre
Contact: Trustee and Administrator –
Mrs M.J. Maltby
Home-care contact: Hospice office –
0945 65778 or Mrs Maltby – 0945
589447

HC, DC, OT, BS, T, AIDS, MND/OTI

★ Home-care service consists of day
sitters. Plans for 6 in-patient beds.

WITHINGTON, MANCHESTER

Macmillan Hospital Support Nurse
*Christie Hospital & Holt Radium
Institute*
Wilmslow Road
Withington
Manchester
M20 9BX
Tel. 061 445 8123

Contact: Macmillan Hospital Support
Nurse – Mrs C. Lawther

★ Advice on pain and symptom control,
support for patients, relatives and staff.
Teaching and counselling.

WIVELSFIELD GREEN, SUSSEX

St Peter's and St James's
North Common Road
Wivelsfield Green
RH17 7RJ
Tel. 044 484 598

Contacts: Medical Officer – Dr Estcourt
Matron – Mrs J. Todman
Sister in Charge – Sister J. Giblin

B – 25 (8 for terminal care)

WOKINGHAM, BERKSHIRE

Macmillan Service
Community Nursing Centre
Wokingham Hospital
Barkham Road
Wokingham
RG11 2RE
Tel. 0734 787843/773287

Location: 200 yards from Wokingham
station
Contact: Senior Nurse – Mrs K. Dungay
Macmillan nurses

HC, BS, NS – 2

WOLVERHAMPTON, WEST MIDLANDS

Compton Hall Hospice
Compton Road West
Compton
Wolverhampton
WV3 9DH
Tel. 0902 758151

Location: 1½ miles east of
Wolverhampton town centre
Catchment: Wolverhampton, Dudley,
Walsall, Sandwell, parts of
Staffordshire, Shropshire,
Bromsgrove, Kidderminster,
Hereford and Worcester
Contact: Bursar – Mr Willam W.
Stockton
Home-care contact: 0902 744800

B – 26, HC, DC, OT/PT, BS, T, AIDS*, MND/OTI,
MD, NS – 80

*Each case considered individually.

WORCESTER, WORCESTERSHIRE

St Richard's Hospice Foundation
Rose Hill House
Rose Hill
London Road
Worcester
Tel. 0905 24879

Location: ½ mile south-east of city centre
off A44
Catchment: Worcester and District
Health Authority
Contacts: Senior Nurse – Mrs Sheila
Gilbert
Administrator – Mr Peter Tebbit
Medical Officers – Dr Judy Dale,
Dr David Jeffrey
Home-care contact: Senior Nurse – Mrs
Sheila Gilbert – 0905 24879

HC, DC, BS, T, AIDS, MND/OTI, NS – 5

WORKINGTON, CUMBRIA

Macmillan Service
Ann Burrow Thomas Health Centre
South William Street
Workington
CA14 2ED
Tel. 0900 602244, ext 166 or 132

Catchment: West Cumbria Health
District
Contact: Nurse Manager – Mrs Margaret
Dowling – 0900 602244, ext 166

HC, BS, AIDS, MND/OTI, NS – 3

WORKSOP, NOTTINGHAMSHIRE

Bassetlaw Hospice of the Good Shepherd Appeal
Barrowby House
Highland Grove
Worksop
Tel. 0909 485321, ext 145

Contact: Hon Secretary – Mr Robert Cockburn

★ Planning for 6-bed unit and day care.

Macmillan Service
Larwood Health Centre
56 Larwood Street
Worksop
S81 0HH
Tel. 0909 500244

HC, AIDS

WORSLEY, MANCHESTER

St Ann's Hospice
Peel Lane
Little Hulton
Worsley
Manchester
M28 6EL
Tel. 061 702 8181

Location: 1½ miles from exit 4 on M61
Catchment: Salford, Bolton, Bury, North Manchester Health Districts
Contacts: Matron – Mrs J.H. Gibbs
Assistant Company Secretary – Mrs A.D. Arrowsmith
Senior Medical Officer – Dr F.O. Wilson
Home-care contact: the patient's GP applies through the Hospice

B – 30, HC, OT/PT, BS, T, AIDS*, MND/OTI, MD, NS – 37.5 WTE

* Will consider AIDS patients if associated with terminal cancer.

WORTHING, WEST SUSSEX

St Barnabas' Hospice
Columbia Drive
Worthing
BN13 2QF
Tel. 0903 64222

Location: Durrington area, west of Worthing, 1 mile south of A27
Catchment: Worthing Area Health Authority
Contact: Bursar – Mr Francis B.C. de Beer
Home-care contact: 0903 64222

B – 26, HC, DC, OT/PT, BS, T, MD, NS – 30 WTE

WREXHAM, CLWYD

Nightingale House
Wrexham Maelor Hospital
Croesnewydd Road
Wrexham
LI13 7TD
Tel. 0978 291100, ext 5224 or 5370

Location: 1 mile from centre of Wrexham
Catchment: Clwyd South
Contact: Dr G.J. Arthurs
Home-care contact: 0978 291100, ext 262

HC, DC, OT/PT, BS, T, MND/OTI, MD, NS – 5

YORK, NORTH YORKSHIRE

Macmillan Service
The Health Centre
31–5 Monkgate
York
YO3 7PB
Tel. 0904 30351, ext 5435/6

HC

St Leonard's Hospice
185 Tadcaster Road
York
YO2 2QL
Tel. 0904 708553/4

Location: 2 miles south-west of city centre on A1036, just inside city boundary
Catchment: York Health District but boundaries are not sacrosanct
Contacts: Matron – Mrs Janet Kay
Medical Director – Dr Susan Collier
Administrator – Wg-Cdr Ron Mason

B – 16, DC, OT/PT, BS, T, MD, NS – 8 f/t & 25 p/t

Illustration sources

The Cancer & Leukaemia in Childhood Trust: opp. p. 128 (above); opp. p. 128 (below); opp. p. 129

© John Cole Impact Photos: opp. p. 32 (below)

Macmillan Fund Press Office: opp. p. 32 (above); opp. p. 33 (above); opp. p. 64 (above); opp. p. 64 (below)

Yoshi Shimazu: opp. p. 33 (below); opp. p. 65 (above); opp. p. 65 (below); opp. p. 96 (above); opp. p. 96 (below); opp. p. 97 (above); opp. p. 97 (below)